Faik Aleskerov
Arkadij Naiditsch

CHESSGAMER

TACTICS AWAKEN

Chess
Evolution

Cover designer
Piotr Pielach
Drawings by Ingram Image

Typesetting
i-Press ‹www.i-press.pl›

First edition 2018 by Chess Evolution

ChessGamer. Tactics awaken
Copyright © 2018 Chess Evolution

ISBN 978-615-5793-05-9

All sales or enquiries should be directed to Chess Evolution
2040 Budaors, Nyar utca 16, Magyarorszag

e-mail: info@chess-evolution.com
website: www.chess-evolution.com

Printed in Hungary

TABLE OF CONTENTS

INTRODUCTION

Dear Reader!

This book covers 10 important chess topics. Each topic is separated into its own chapter and each chapter is constructed in the following way: 2 illustrative positions with solutions, an explanation of the topic and some help and hints to help the reader solve the exercises. There are 40 exercises, growing in difficulty, starting with the easy ones and finishing with the most complicated. The solutions for each chapter can be found at the very end of the book.

After you have worked through the 10 topics, you will find yourself at the test section, where you can challenge your new-found knowledge. There are 8 tests, each consisting of 10 positions, with one position from each of the topics that we covered in this book. However, you won't know which position belongs to which topic!

The solutions to the tests can also be found at the very end of the book. The book contains 500 educational positions: 20 exemplary positions, 400 exercises and 80 test positions.

While you are going through the exercises, you will sometimes run into the following smiley:

When you meet with this smiley, it means that you must take a deeper look into the position. It could be that the most obvious move is not the best one, or the key move comes later, not on the first move, and you need to foresee it. In each position White is to move. When you see "1. +-", it means White to move and win. When you see "1. =", it means White to move and make a draw.

We wish you a lot of fun reading our book, and we hope that the motifs you will learn in this book will prove very useful in your own games as well!

EDITORIAL PREFACE

The first chess game your authors played against each other was at the World Junior under 10 championship, now more than 22 years ago. Since then a lot of time may have passed, but one thing has remained — we both still love chess and are both still involved in playing and training!

With our first book in the series ChessGamer — "Tactics awaken" — we would like to introduce a learning concept, one which we think is the best among many and which places the emphasis on an effective and practical chess education.

To us, chess is a combination of sport, art and science. To be a good chess player and show improvement, you need to have a feel for the game, combined with being passionate about it — and there is nothing that brings young players more fun and enjoyment than solving chess puzzles.

By having 10 different topics, the current book will improve your various tactical skills and imagination a lot.

Every professional player knows that the most important factor in chess is good, stable calculation. You can play a great game and reduce all your efforts to dust in just one move, so precise, fast calculation helps you to avoid big errors — a major factor in every game you play.

As in every sport, chess is about winning. A game that might last up to 7 hours straight is very emotional, and a tournament win stays forever in the memory (as well as some losses!) but this is what chess is about. We all play with the same pieces, with the same rules, and the better player wins having no influence from outside.

We tried to give our very best here to create educational material that combines fun and the learning process into one. Enjoy solving the puzzles, learning new ideas and using them in your practical games!

Arkadij Naiditsch   Faik Aleskerov
International Grandmaster   International Master (elect)

CHAPTER 1.
MATE IN ONE MOVE

In this chapter, we are going to solve 'mate in one move' problems. Checkmate occurs when a player's king is directly attacked by an opponent's piece or pawn and has no possible move to escape the check. There are three escape possibilities: Moving away from the check with the king, capturing the piece which is giving the check, or moving a piece in-between the king and the piece which is giving the check. If none of these is possible, the side who gives checkmate wins the game.

There is no way to escape from the check, therefore it is checkmate.

Example 2

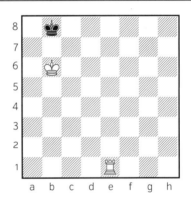

1. ♖e8#

After this rook check the king has no square to move to, so it is checkmate! In this chapter you need to deliver such checkmates in one move, but in more-and-more complicated positions as the chapter progresses.

Example 1

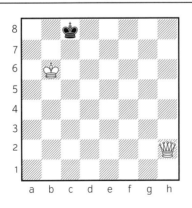

1. ♕c7#

if he gos thar 2 tims
you go back

PUZZLE 1

PUZZLE 2

kh + sos tare

if H gos thare
you go thare

1. +-

if H gos thare
you go thare

1. +-   e5

you go thare
2b 2c
2d

PUZZLE 3

PUZZLE 4

1. +- The Bishup
upright then
check mate
C6

1. +- 1 of the
hores gos
up
98

PUZZLE 5

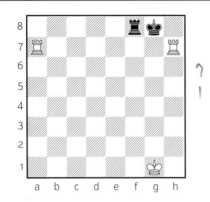

1. +-   h8

PUZZLE 6

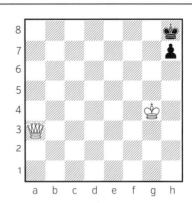

1. +-   c3 = f8

PUZZLE 7

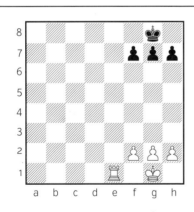

1. +- The rook
goes left
then up
e8

PUZZLE 8

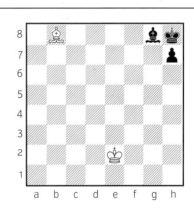

1. +- The Bishup
goes down
3 spaces
down he5

PUZZLE 9

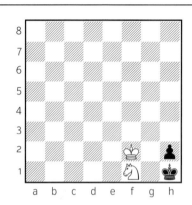

1. +- *93*

PUZZLE 10

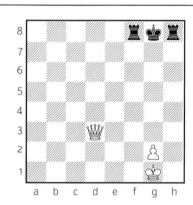

1. +- *C4*

PUZZLE 11

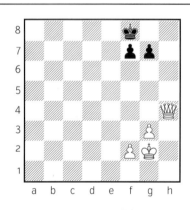

1. +- *C8*

PUZZLE 12

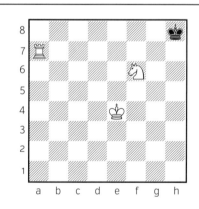

1. +- *e5*

PUZZLE 13

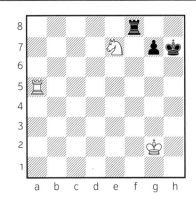

1. +-   a 6 - h 5

PUZZLE 14

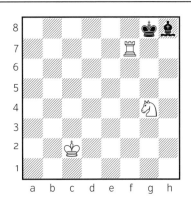

1. +-   g 5

PUZZLE 15

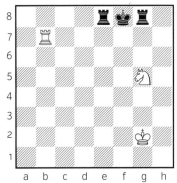

1. +-   F 7

PUZZLE 16

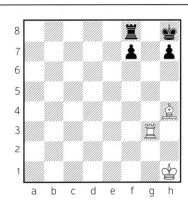

1. +-   F 6

PUZZLE 17

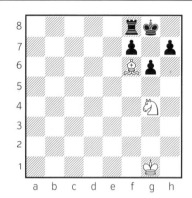

1. +- *Nh6*

PUZZLE 18

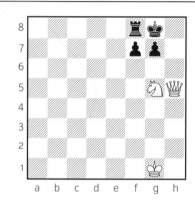

1. +- *e7*

PUZZLE 19

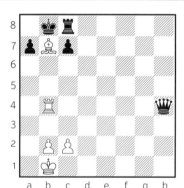

1. +- *be4#*

PUZZLE 20

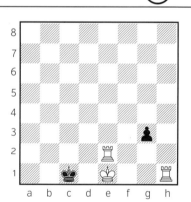

1. +- *0-0*

PUZZLE 21

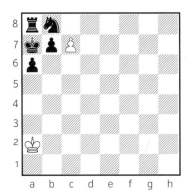

1. +- C8n#

PUZZLE 22

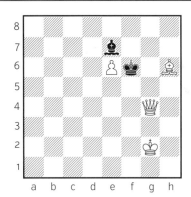

1. +- Qf×4

PUZZLE 23

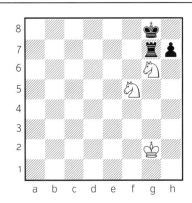

1. +- He7

PUZZLE 24

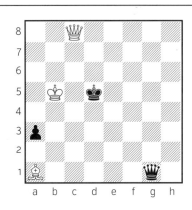

1. +- D8

PUZZLE 25

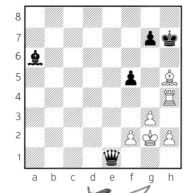

1. +-

PUZZLE 26

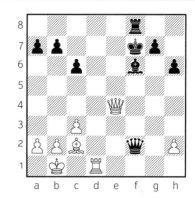

1. +- bb3#

PUZZLE 27

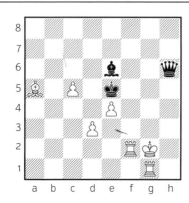

1. +- BC7#

PUZZLE 28

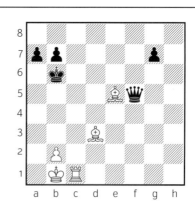

1. +- Bd4#

PUZZLE 29

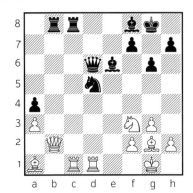

1. +- Q h 8 #

PUZZLE 30

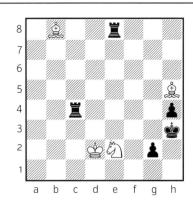

1. +- N 41+ #

PUZZLE 31

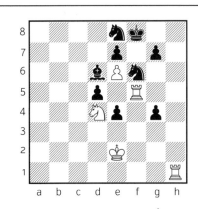

1. +- R f 6 X#

PUZZLE 32

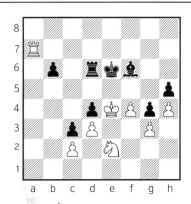

1. +- N d4x #

Kayvon

PUZZLE 33

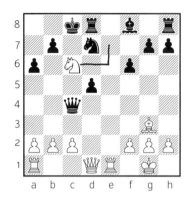

1. +- He7x #

PUZZLE 34

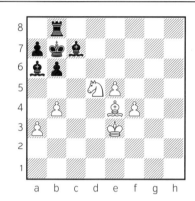

1. +- K e7#

PUZZLE 35

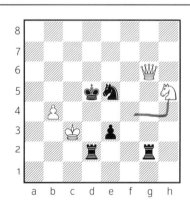

1. +- Hosef4 X #

PUZZLE 36

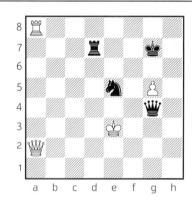

1. +- R98X #

PUZZLE 37

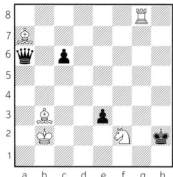

1. +- BB8X#

PUZZLE 38

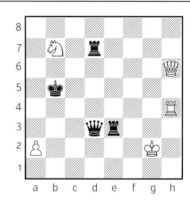

1. +- QH5X#

PUZZLE 39

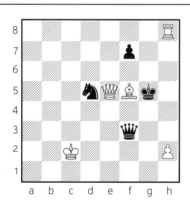

1. +- QE7#

PUZZLE 40

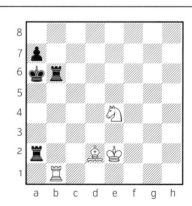

1. +- HC5X#

CHAPTER 2.
MATE IN TWO MOVES

Example 1

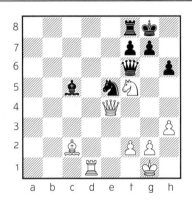

Example 2

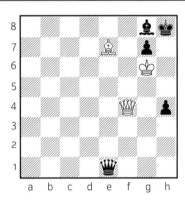

In this chapter we need to deliver checkmate in two moves! We are looking forward to lots of sacrifices.

1.♘e7+ ♕xe7 2.♕h7#

1.♕h6+

After this beautiful queen sacrifice, checkmate is inevitable on the next move!

1...gxh6

1...♗h7+ 2.♕xh7#

2.♗f6#

A unique mate! Use your imagination and solve the puzzles!

PUZZLE 1

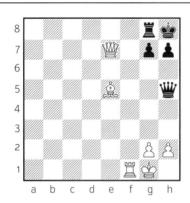

1. +-   Qg7+
        rf8#

PUZZLE 2

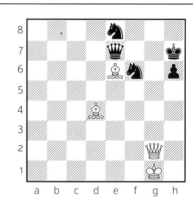

1. +-   Bf5X

PUZZLE 3

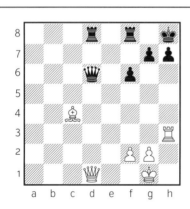

1. +-   rh7+
        Qh5#

PUZZLE 4

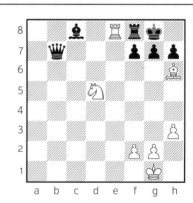

1. +-   Ke7+
        rf8#

PUZZLE 5

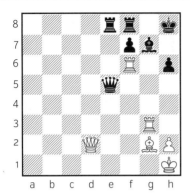

1. +−

PUZZLE 6

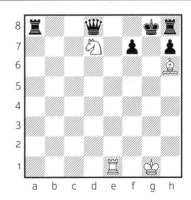

1. +−

PUZZLE 7

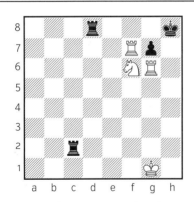

1. +−

PUZZLE 8

1. +−

PUZZLE 9

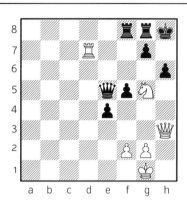

1. +–

PUZZLE 10

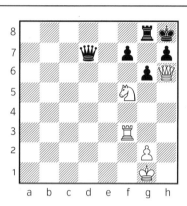

1. +–

PUZZLE 11

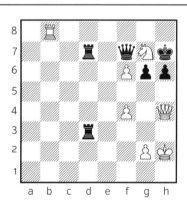

1. +–

PUZZLE 12

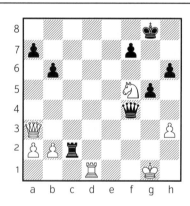

1. +–

PUZZLE 13

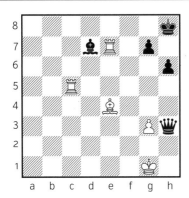

1. +—

PUZZLE 14

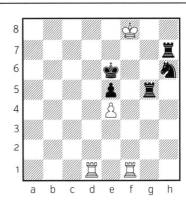

1. +—

PUZZLE 15

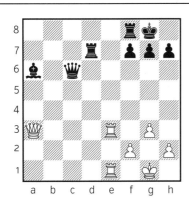

1. +—

PUZZLE 16

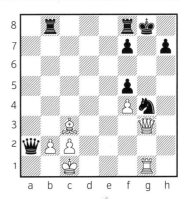

1. +— Qg4

PUZZLE 17

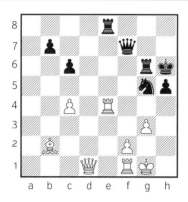

1. +– ....

....

PUZZLE 18

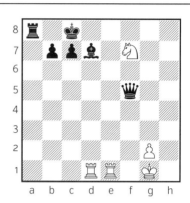

1. +– ....

....

PUZZLE 19

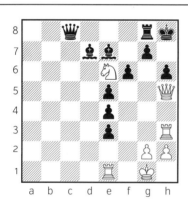

1. +– ....

....

PUZZLE 20

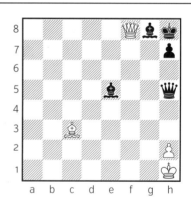

1. +– ....

....

PUZZLE 21

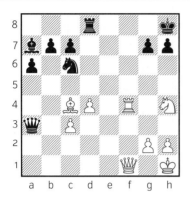

1. +–

PUZZLE 22

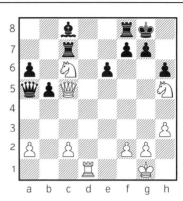

1. +–

PUZZLE 23

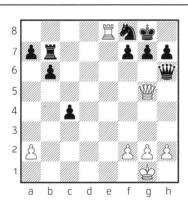

1. +–

PUZZLE 24

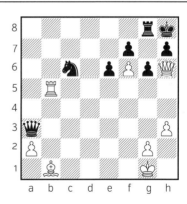

1. +–

PUZZLE 25

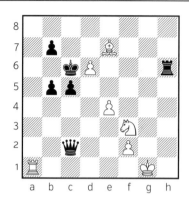

1. +–

PUZZLE 26

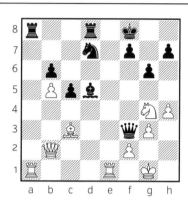

1. +–

PUZZLE 27

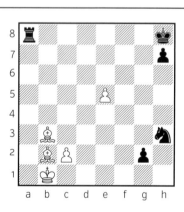

1. +–

PUZZLE 28

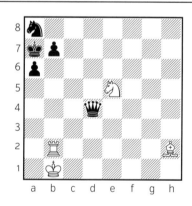

1. +–

PUZZLE 29

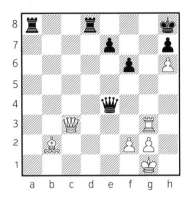

1. +– ....

....

PUZZLE 30

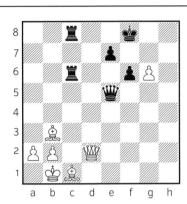

1. +– ....

....

PUZZLE 31

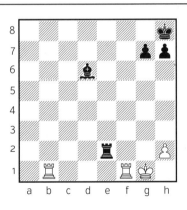

1. +– ....

....

PUZZLE 32

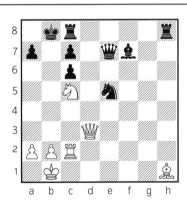

1. +– ....

....

PUZZLE 33

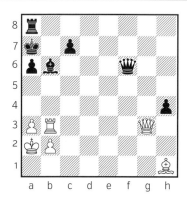

1. +–

PUZZLE 34

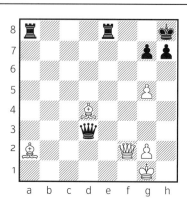

1. +–

PUZZLE 35

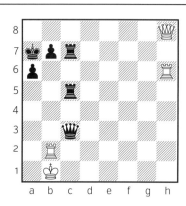

1. +–

PUZZLE 36

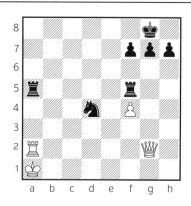

1. +–

PUZZLE 37

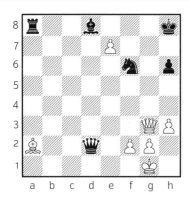

1. +– ....

....

PUZZLE 38

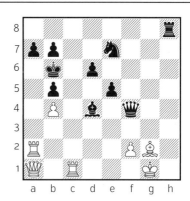

1. +– ....

....

PUZZLE 39

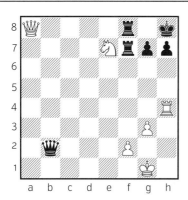

1. +– ....

....

PUZZLE 40

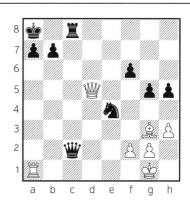

1. +– ....

....

CHAPTER 3.
MATE USING THE PIN

Example 1

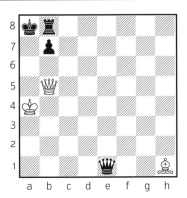

Example 2

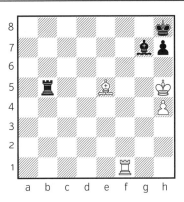

The pin is one of the most common motifs in chess. It arises when a defending piece cannot move without exposing a more valuable defending piece behind it to capture by the attacking piece. In this position, the b7 pawn is pinned by the bishop on h1 and the pawn cannot leave its position because the king on a8 would be under attack. Therefore White can deliver mate in one move by playing...

1. ♕a6#

The king has no square to escape to and the pawn is pinned!

The e5-bishop is pinned by the rook on b5 — it cannot move because the king on h5 remains unprotected and attacked. Black attacks the bishop with two pieces and it seems like he is going to win it. However, the g7-bishop is also pinned by the e5-bishop as the king on h8 comes under attack otherwise. White, to move, can make use of this pin by playing...

1. ♖f8#

Checkmate! In this chapter, you need to deliver similar checkmates in one move making use of a pin — again in more-and-more difficult positions.

PUZZLE 1

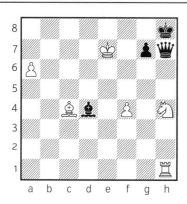

1. +–

PUZZLE 2

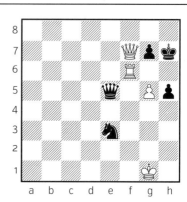

1. +–

PUZZLE 3

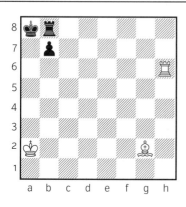

1. +–

PUZZLE 4

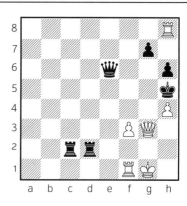

1. +–

PUZZLE 5

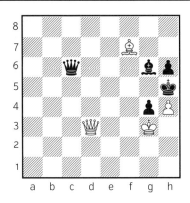

1. +– ....

....

PUZZLE 6

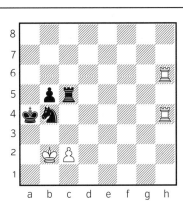

1. +– ....

....

PUZZLE 7

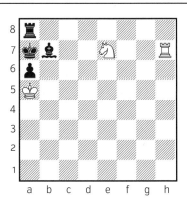

1. +– ....

....

PUZZLE 8

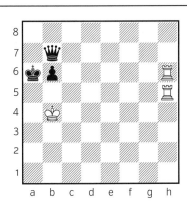

1. +– ....

....

PUZZLE 9

1. +−

PUZZLE 10

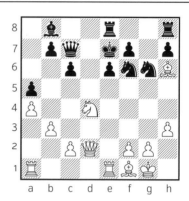

1. +−

PUZZLE 11

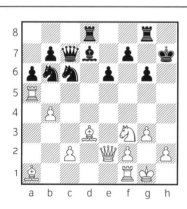

1. +−

PUZZLE 12

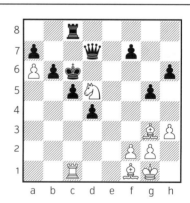

1. +−

PUZZLE 13

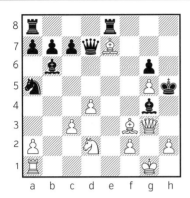

1. +−

PUZZLE 14

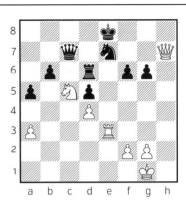

1. +−

PUZZLE 15

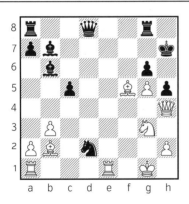

1. +−

PUZZLE 16

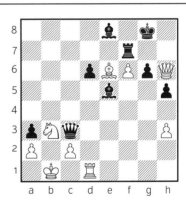

1. +−

PUZZLE 17

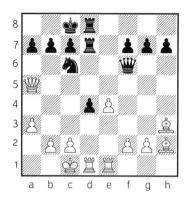

1. +–

PUZZLE 18

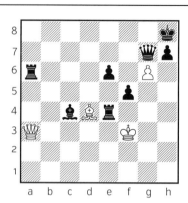

1. +–

PUZZLE 19

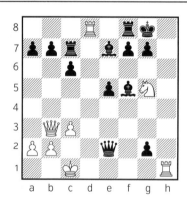

1. +–

PUZZLE 20

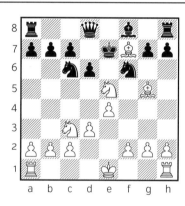

1. +–

PUZZLE 21

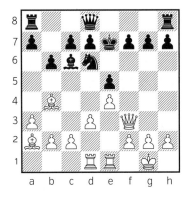

1. +–
....

....

PUZZLE 22

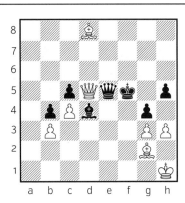

1. +–
....

....

PUZZLE 23

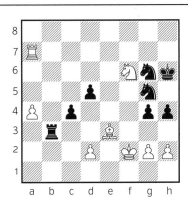

1. +–
....

....

PUZZLE 24

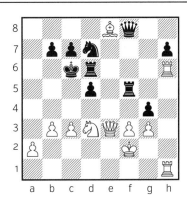

1. +–
....

....

PUZZLE 25

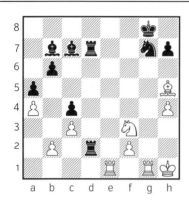

1. +−

PUZZLE 26

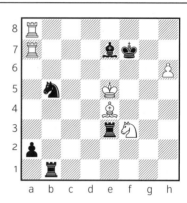

1. +−

PUZZLE 27

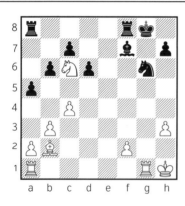

1. +−

PUZZLE 28

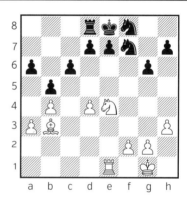

1. +−

PUZZLE 29

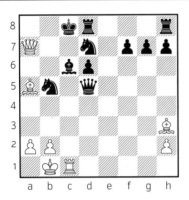

1. +– ....

....

PUZZLE 30

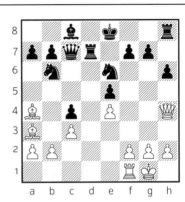

1. +– ....

....

PUZZLE 31

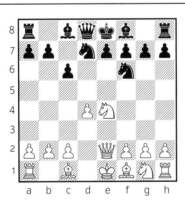

1. +– ....

....

PUZZLE 32

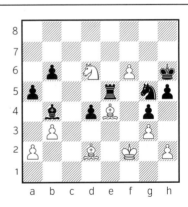

1. +– ....

....

PUZZLE 33

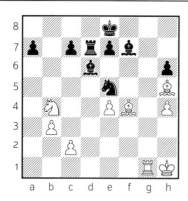

1. +—

PUZZLE 34

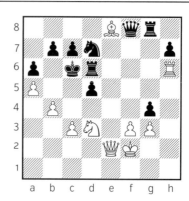

1. +—

PUZZLE 35

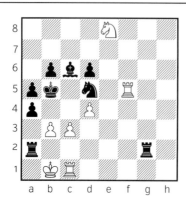

1. +—

PUZZLE 36

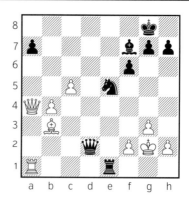

1. +—

PUZZLE 37

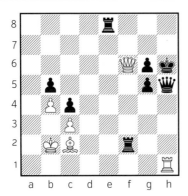

1. +– ....

....

PUZZLE 38

1. +– ....

....

PUZZLE 39

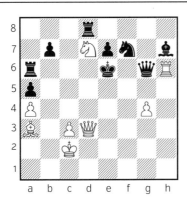

1. +– ....

....

PUZZLE 40

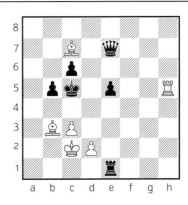

1. +– ....

....

CHAPTER 4.
SMOTHERED MATE

Example 1

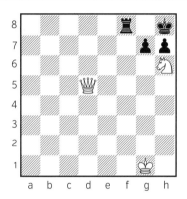

White to move and give mate in two moves!

1.♕g8+ ♖xg8 2.♘f7#

A picturesque checkmate! With the fantastic queen sacrifice on the first move, White has squeezed the black king into the corner and the knight delivered mate! This is called smothered mate as the king cannot move because of his own pieces. We should remember well this motif because this is the most common way to deliver smothered mates.

Example 2

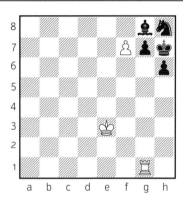

1.f8♘#

Smothered mate by underpromotion! Instead of promoting to a queen, White promotes to a knight and gives checkmate in one move as all the possible squares of the black king are blocked by his own pieces. We should never forget about underpromotion — sometimes such 'promotion with check' can be decisive, although in most cases we should stick to making a new queen as she is the most valuable piece. In this chapter, you will need to deliver such kinds of checkmates in different and increasingly complicated situations.

PUZZLE 1

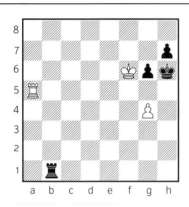

1. +−

PUZZLE 2

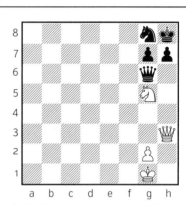

1. +−

PUZZLE 3

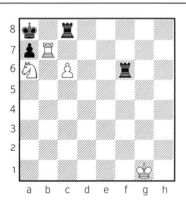

1. +−

PUZZLE 4

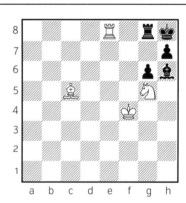

1. +−

PUZZLE 5

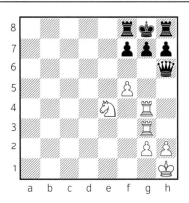

1. +–

PUZZLE 6

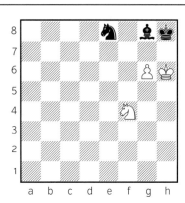

1. +–

PUZZLE 7

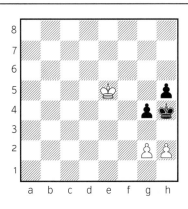

1. +–

PUZZLE 8

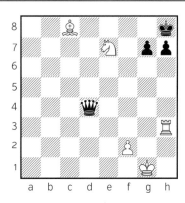

1. +–

PUZZLE 9

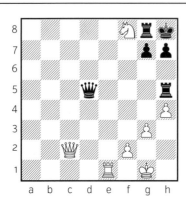

1. +–

PUZZLE 10

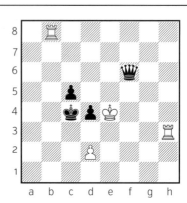

1. +–

PUZZLE 11

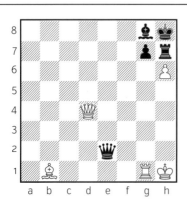

1. +–

PUZZLE 12

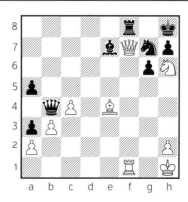

1. +–

PUZZLE 13

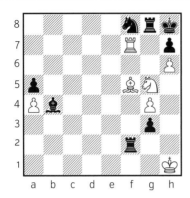

1. +–

....

....

PUZZLE 14

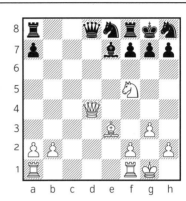

1. +–

....

....

PUZZLE 15

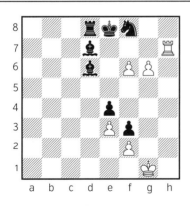

1. +–

....

....

PUZZLE 16

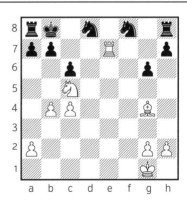

1. +–

....

....

PUZZLE 17

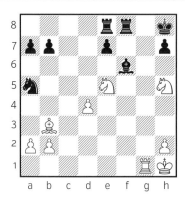

1. +–

PUZZLE 18

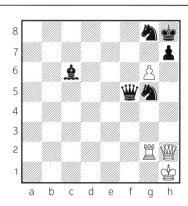

1. +–

PUZZLE 19

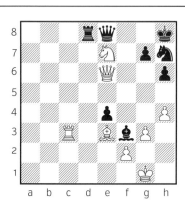

1. +–

PUZZLE 20

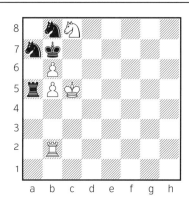

1. +–

PUZZLE 21

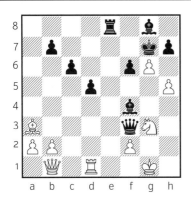

1. +– ....

....

PUZZLE 22

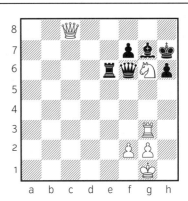

1. +– ....

....

PUZZLE 23

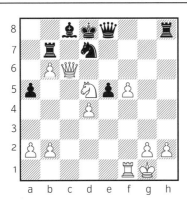

1. +– ....

....

PUZZLE 24

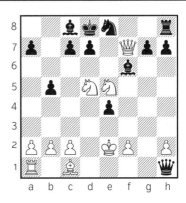

1. +– ....

....

PUZZLE 25

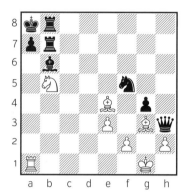

1. +–

PUZZLE 26

1. +–

PUZZLE 27

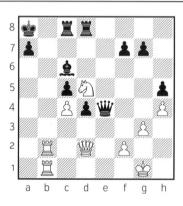

1. +–

PUZZLE 28

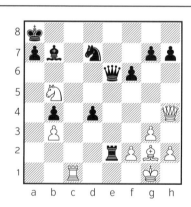

1. +–

PUZZLE 29

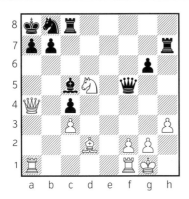

1. +– ....

....

PUZZLE 30

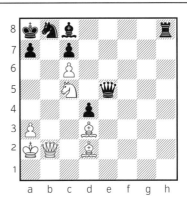

1. +– ....

....

PUZZLE 31

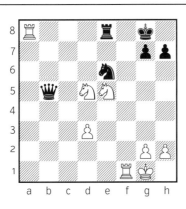

1. +– ....

....

PUZZLE 32

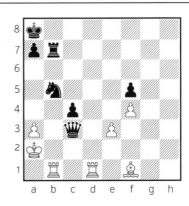

1. +– ....

....

PUZZLE 33

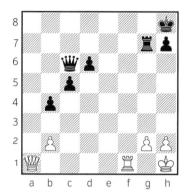

1. +–
....
....

PUZZLE 34

1. +–
....
....

PUZZLE 35

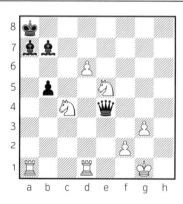

1. +–
....
....

PUZZLE 36

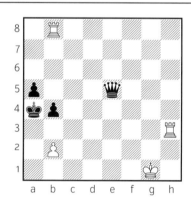

1. +–
....
....

PUZZLE 37

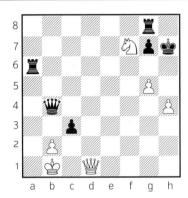

1. +– ....

....

PUZZLE 38

1. +– ....

....

PUZZLE 39

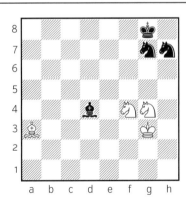

1. +– ....

....

PUZZLE 40

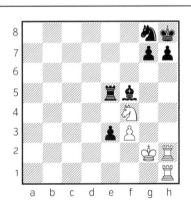

1. +– ....

....

CHAPTER 5.
MATE WITH DOUBLECHECK

Example 1

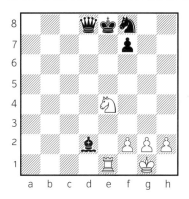

Example 2

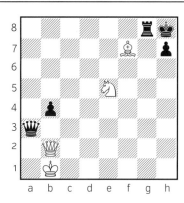

White to move and checkmate in one move!

1.♘f6#

Doublecheck and checkmate! White gives two checks at the same time — with the rook and the knight. Both pieces could be taken but the other one keeps the king in check, therefore it is not possible. The only escape would be to move away from the check with the king, but there are no squares available!

1.♘g6#

Doublecheck and checkmate again! White gives two checks at the same time, which means that it is not possible to take either of the pieces — despite them both hanging — and the king has no square to run to. Doublecheck is a very strong weapon in chess and we always need to pay attention to such possibilities. In this chapter you need to deliver checkmates with the help of a doublecheck.

PUZZLE 1

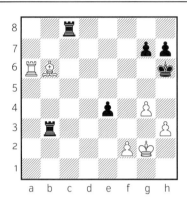

1. +−

PUZZLE 2

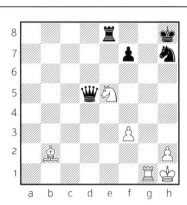

1. +−

PUZZLE 3

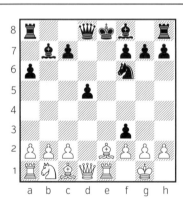

1. +−

PUZZLE 4

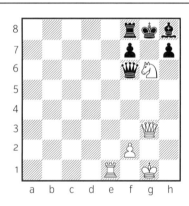

1. +−

PUZZLE 5

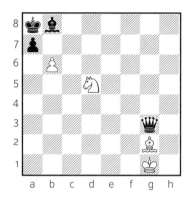

1. +−

PUZZLE 6

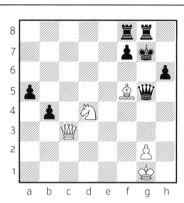

1. +−

PUZZLE 7

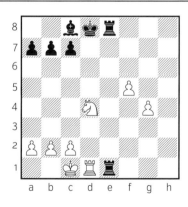

1. +−

PUZZLE 8

1. +−

PUZZLE 9

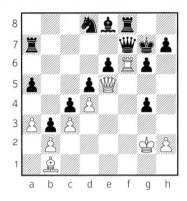

1. +–

PUZZLE 10

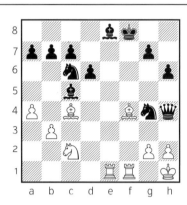

1. +–

PUZZLE 11

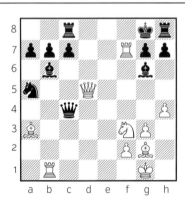

1. +–

PUZZLE 12

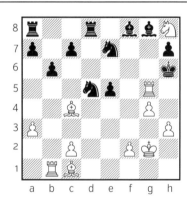

1. +–

PUZZLE 13

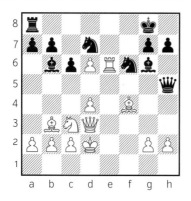

1. +–

....

....

PUZZLE 14

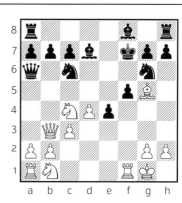

1. +–

....

....

PUZZLE 15

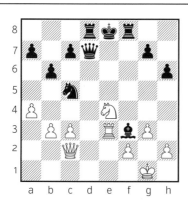

1. +–

....

....

PUZZLE 16

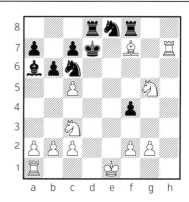

1. +–

....

....

PUZZLE 17

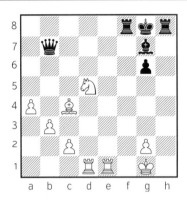

1. +–

PUZZLE 18

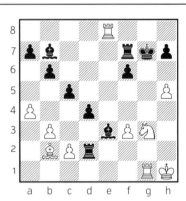

1. +–

PUZZLE 19

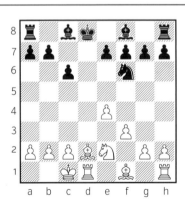

1. +–

PUZZLE 20

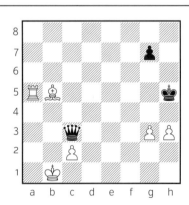

1. +–

PUZZLE 21

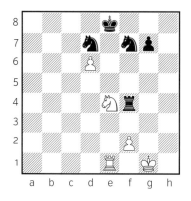

1. +–

PUZZLE 22

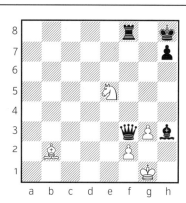

1. +–

PUZZLE 23

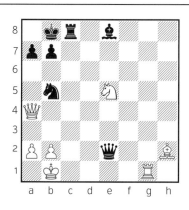

1. +–

PUZZLE 24

1. +–

PUZZLE 25

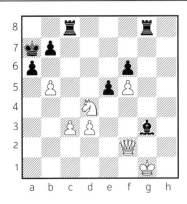

1. +–

PUZZLE 26

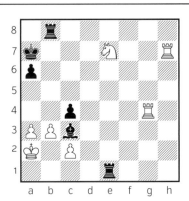

1. +–

PUZZLE 27

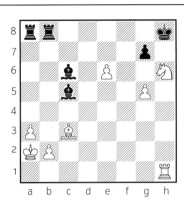

1. +–

PUZZLE 28

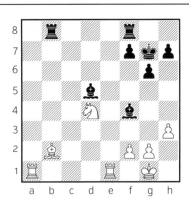

1. +–

PUZZLE 29

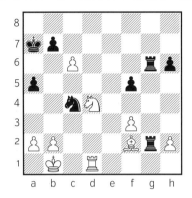

1. +– ....

....

PUZZLE 30

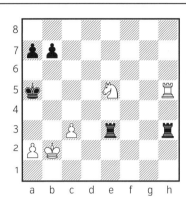

1. +– ....

....

PUZZLE 31

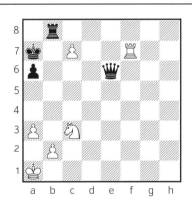

1. +– ....

....

PUZZLE 32

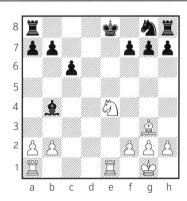

1. +– ....

....

PUZZLE 33

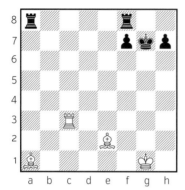

1. +–
....
....

PUZZLE 34

1. +–
....
....

PUZZLE 35

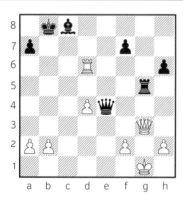

1. +–
....
....

PUZZLE 36

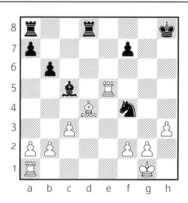

1. +–
....
....

PUZZLE 37

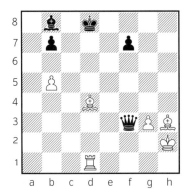

1. +−

PUZZLE 38

1. +−

PUZZLE 39

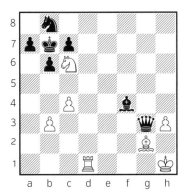

1. +−

PUZZLE 40

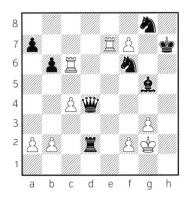

1. +−

CHAPTER 6.
STALEMATE

Example 1

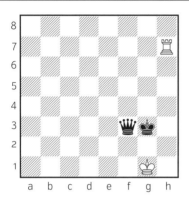

Stalemate is a situation where the player whose turn it is to move is not in check, but has no legal move to continue the game. The rules of chess state that when stalemate occurs, the game ends as a draw (i.e. having no winner). During the endgame, stalemate is a resource that can enable the player with the inferior position to draw the game rather than lose. In this position, White seems to have a lost endgame, however he can save the game with a stalemate motif!

1.♖h3+

White either captures the queen next move, or after...

1...♔xh3=

White is not in check and he has no move, therefore the game is drawn by stalemate!

Example 2

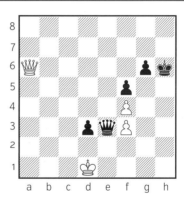

White seems to be in huge trouble as ♕e2 check is going to be decisive, however here again a stalemate idea saves him:

1.♕xg6+ ♔xg6=

Compared to the previous position, White has two pawns on the board, but it doesn't change the situation — White has no legal move! In endgames, we should always pay attention to stalemate ideas. They are usually very unexpected, therefore it is very easy to miss them — both as the attacking and defensive side.

PUZZLE 1

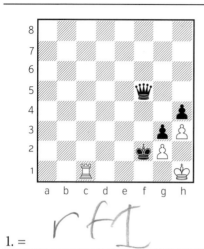

1. =

PUZZLE 2

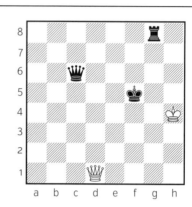

1. =

PUZZLE 3

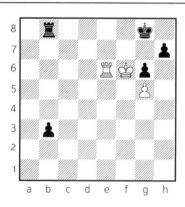

1. =

PUZZLE 4

1. =

PUZZLE 5

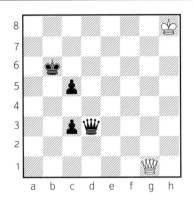

1. =

....

....

PUZZLE 6

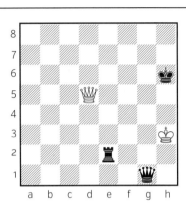

1. =

....

....

PUZZLE 7

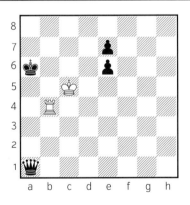

1. =

....

....

PUZZLE 8

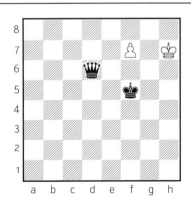

1. =

....

....

PUZZLE 9

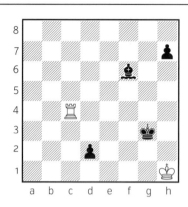

1. =
....

....

PUZZLE 10

1. =
....

....

PUZZLE 11

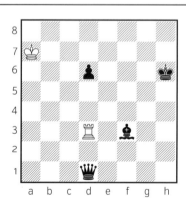

1. =
....

....

PUZZLE 12

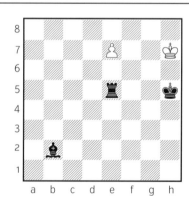

1. =
....

....

PUZZLE 13

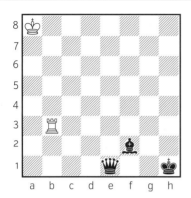

1. =

....

....

PUZZLE 14

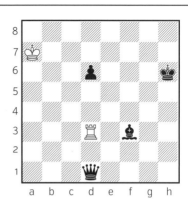

1. =

....

....

PUZZLE 15

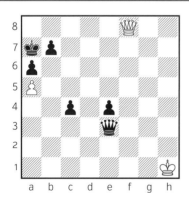

1. =

....

....

PUZZLE 16

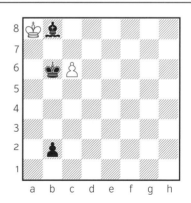

1. =

....

....

PUZZLE 17

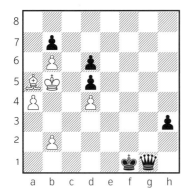

1. =

....

....

PUZZLE 18

1. =

....

....

PUZZLE 19

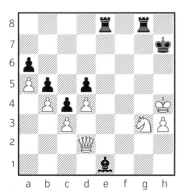

1. =

....

....

PUZZLE 20

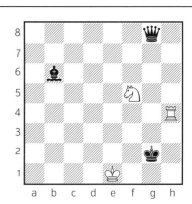

1. =

....

....

PUZZLE 21

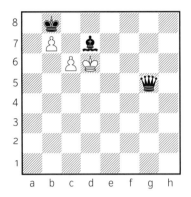

1. =

PUZZLE 22

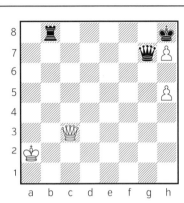

1. =

PUZZLE 23

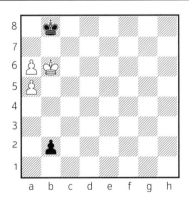

1. =

PUZZLE 24

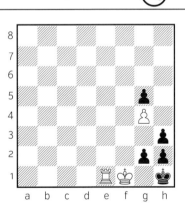

1. =

PUZZLE 25

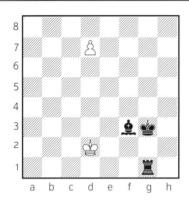

1. =

....

....

PUZZLE 26

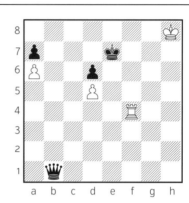

1. =

....

....

PUZZLE 27

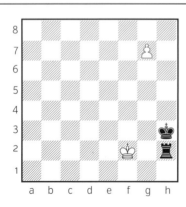

1. =

....

....

PUZZLE 28

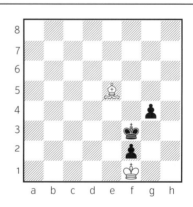

1. =

....

....

PUZZLE 29

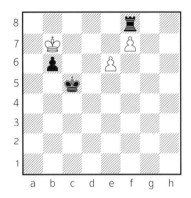

1. = ...

....

PUZZLE 30

1. = ...

....

PUZZLE 31

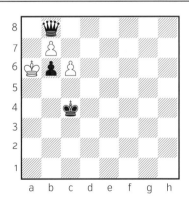

1. = ...

....

PUZZLE 32

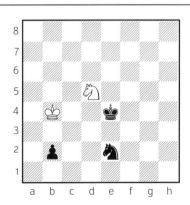

1. = ...

....

PUZZLE 33

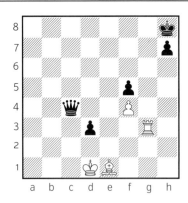

1. = ...

....

PUZZLE 34

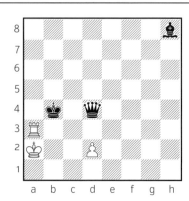

1. = ...

....

PUZZLE 35

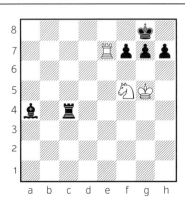

1. = ...

....

PUZZLE 36

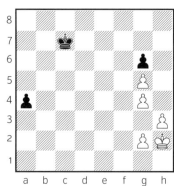

1. = ...

....

PUZZLE 37

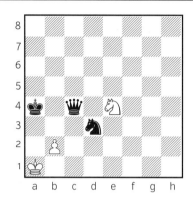

1. = ...

....

PUZZLE 38

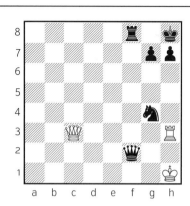

1. = ...

....

PUZZLE 39

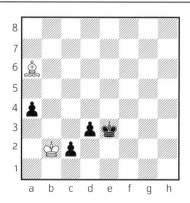

1. = ...

....

PUZZLE 40

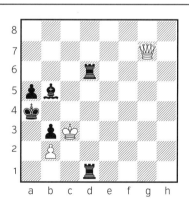

1. = ...

....

CHAPTER 7.
WINNING MATERIAL IN TWO MOVES

Example 1

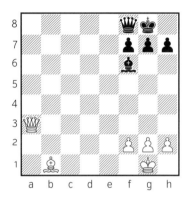

Example 2

In this chapter our task is to win material with the use of a sacrifice!

1.♗xh7+

Deflection! White sacrifices his bishop to lure the black king away from the protection of the f8-queen.

1...♔xh7 2.♕xf8+−

At first sight it seems like the game will soon end in a draw, as Black is going to win the f7-pawn which has been stopped just before the promotion square by the rook on f6. However this rook can be deflected from f6 with

1.♖h6

By pinning the f6 rook, the queening of the f7 pawn is inevitable.

1...♖xh6 2.f8♕++−

In this chapter, you will need to find the way to win material in ever-more complex situations.

PUZZLE 1

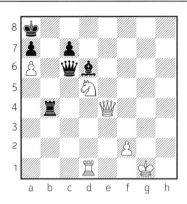

1. +−

PUZZLE 2

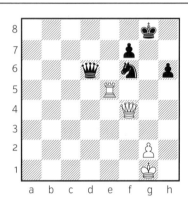

1. +−

PUZZLE 3

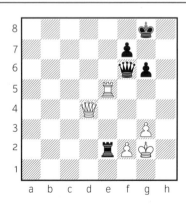

1. +−

PUZZLE 4

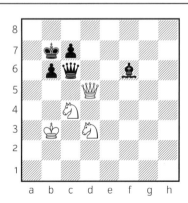

1. +−

PUZZLE 5

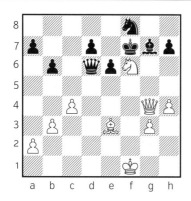

1. +−

PUZZLE 6

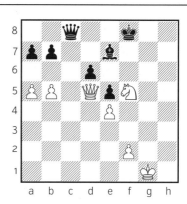

1. +−

PUZZLE 7

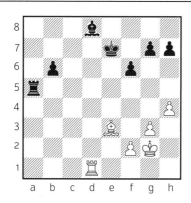

1. +−

PUZZLE 8

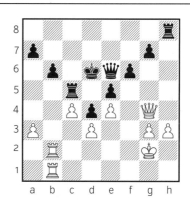

1. +−

PUZZLE 9

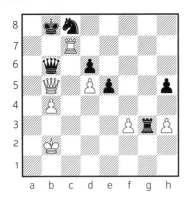

1. +–

PUZZLE 10

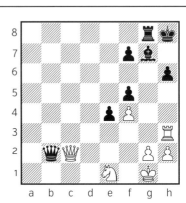

1. +–

PUZZLE 11

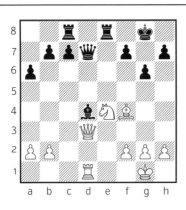

1. +–

PUZZLE 12

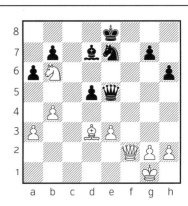

1. +–

PUZZLE 13

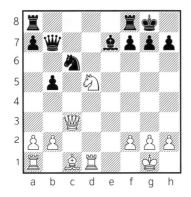

1. +−

PUZZLE 14

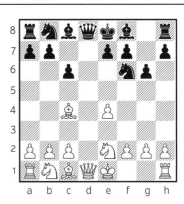

1. +−

PUZZLE 15

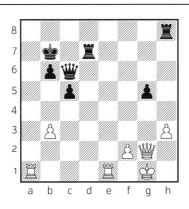

1. +−

PUZZLE 16

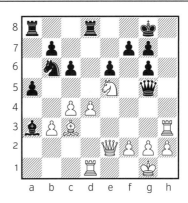

1. +−

PUZZLE 17

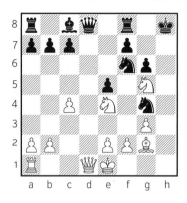

1. +–

PUZZLE 18

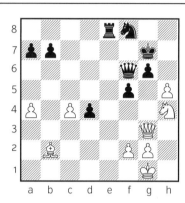

1. +–

PUZZLE 19

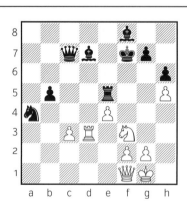

1. +–

PUZZLE 20

1. +–

PUZZLE 21

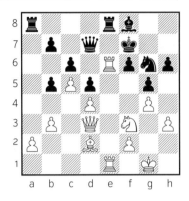

1. +– ....

....

PUZZLE 22

1. +– ....

....

PUZZLE 23

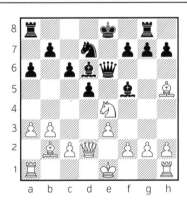

1. +– ....

....

PUZZLE 24

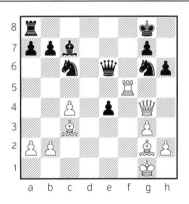

1. +– ....

....

PUZZLE 25

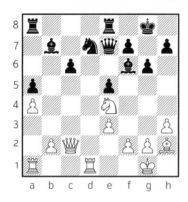

1. +–

PUZZLE 26

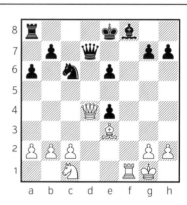

1. +–

PUZZLE 27

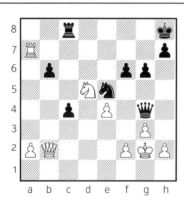

1. +–

PUZZLE 28

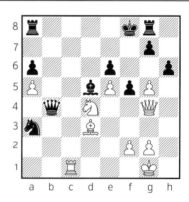

1. +–

PUZZLE 29

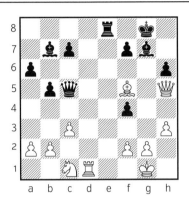

1. +−

PUZZLE 30

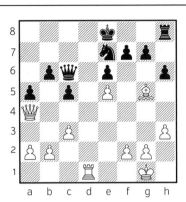

1. +−

PUZZLE 31

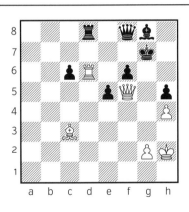

1. +−

PUZZLE 32

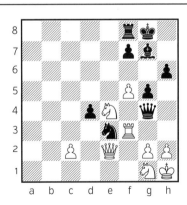

1. +−

PUZZLE 33

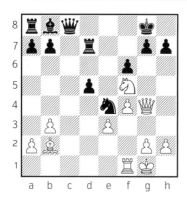

1. +–

PUZZLE 34

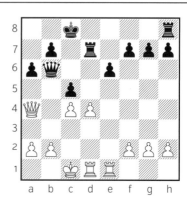

1. +–

PUZZLE 35

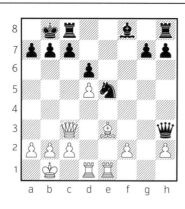

1. +–

PUZZLE 36

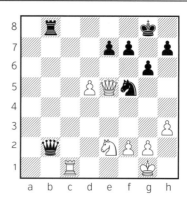

1. +–

PUZZLE 37

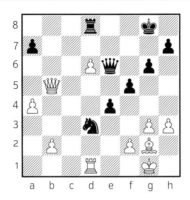

1. +−

PUZZLE 38

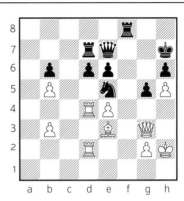

1. +−

PUZZLE 39

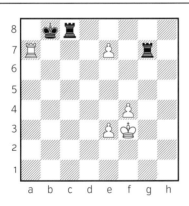

1. +−

PUZZLE 40

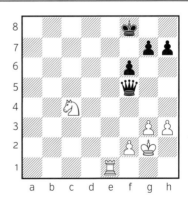

1. +−

CHAPTER 8.
PIN

Example 1

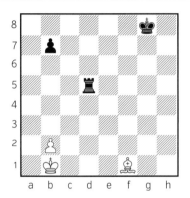

In the 3rd chapter we already became familiar with the pin. There we delivered checkmates in one move with the help of a pin, whereas now we need to try to find a way to win material using this motif.

1. ♗c4+−

White takes the rook next move as it is pinned and cannot move.

Example 2

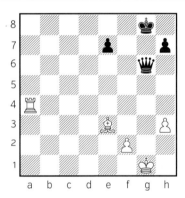

Black has a material advantage for the moment, but after...

1. ♖g4+−

White wins the queen with his rook as she cannot leave because of the pin. The same is true in the opposite way — the rook is also pinned to his own king — but of course this deal favors White as the queen is more valuable than the rook. Try to solve the following exercises with the help of a pin.

PUZZLE 1

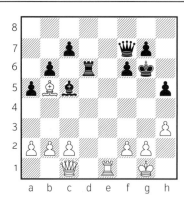

1. +−

PUZZLE 2

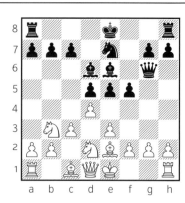

1. +−

PUZZLE 3

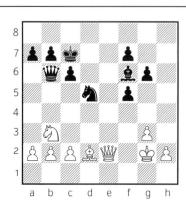

1. +−

PUZZLE 4

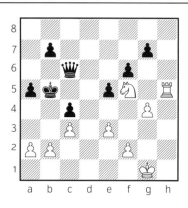

1. +−

PUZZLE 5

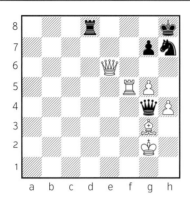

1. +— ....

....

PUZZLE 6

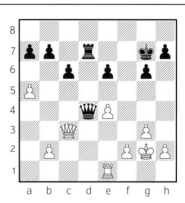

1. +— ....

....

PUZZLE 7

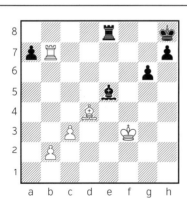

1. +— ....

....

PUZZLE 8

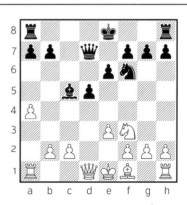

1. +— ....

....

PUZZLE 9

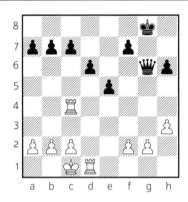

1. +– ....

....

PUZZLE 10

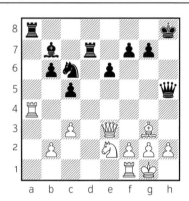

1. +– ....

....

PUZZLE 11

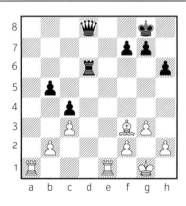

1. +– ....

....

PUZZLE 12

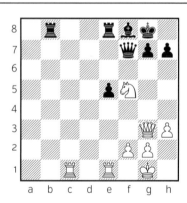

1. +– ....

....

PUZZLE 13

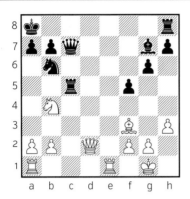

1. +— ....

....

PUZZLE 14

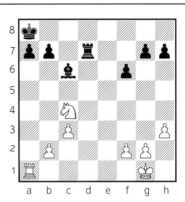

1. +— ....

....

PUZZLE 15

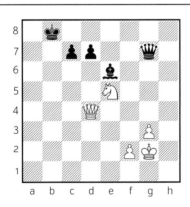

1. +— ....

....

PUZZLE 16

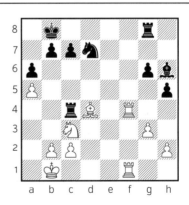

1. +— ....

....

PUZZLE 17

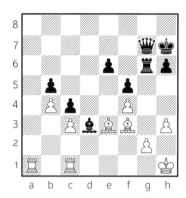

1. +–

....

....

PUZZLE 18

1. +–

....

....

PUZZLE 19

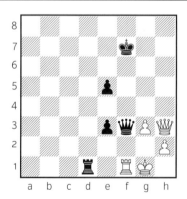

1. +–

....

....

PUZZLE 20

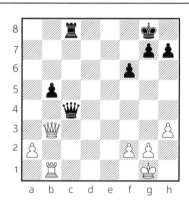

1. +–

....

....

PUZZLE 21

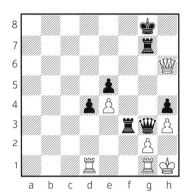

1. +−

PUZZLE 22

1. +−

PUZZLE 23

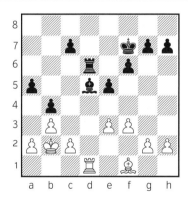

1. +−

PUZZLE 24

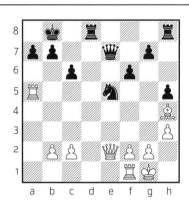

1. +−

PUZZLE 25

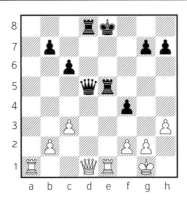

1. +– ....

....

PUZZLE 26

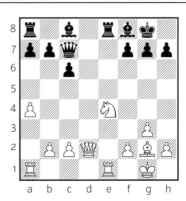

1. +– ....

....

PUZZLE 27

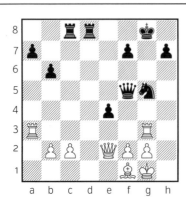

1. +– ....

....

PUZZLE 28

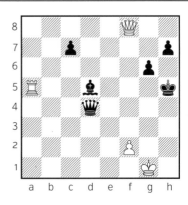

1. +– ....

....

PUZZLE 29

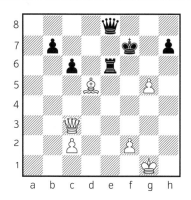

1. +–

PUZZLE 30

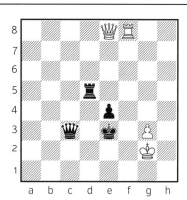

1. +–

PUZZLE 31

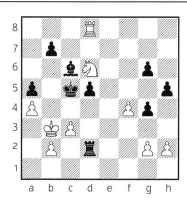

1. +–

PUZZLE 32

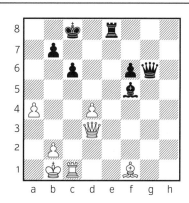

1. +–

PUZZLE 33

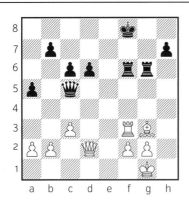

1. +– ....

....

PUZZLE 34

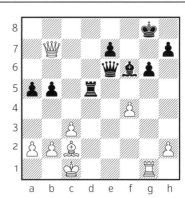

1. +– ....

....

PUZZLE 35

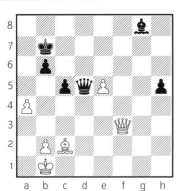

1. +– ....

....

PUZZLE 36

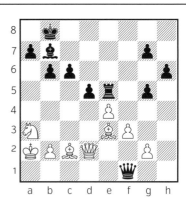

1. +– ....

....

PUZZLE 37

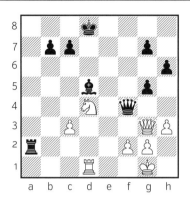

1. +–

....

....

PUZZLE 38

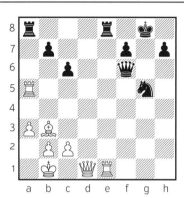

1. +–

....

....

PUZZLE 39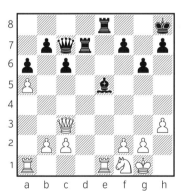

1. +–

....

....

PUZZLE 40

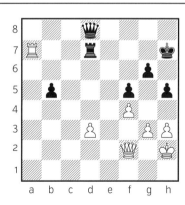

1. +–

....

....

CHAPTER 9.
SKEWER

Example 1

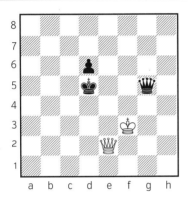

Example 2

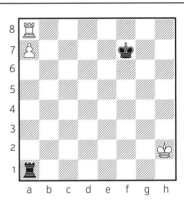

In chess, a skewer is an attack upon two pieces in a line and is similar to a pin. A skewer is sometimes described as a "reverse pin"; the difference is that in a skewer, the more valuable piece is in front of the piece of lesser value. The opponent is compelled to move the more valuable piece to avoid its capture, thereby exposing the less valuable piece which can then be captured. The current position is a typical skewer:

1.♕b5+

White gives a check and forces the king away, leaving the queen to fall "for free".

1...♔e6 2.♕xg5+−

If it was Black's turn, we would reach a theoretically-drawn endgame after ...♔g7. However the current misplacement of the black king allows White to win the game by using the skewer motif!

1.♖h8

White intends to promote his pawn which would mean the end of the game, and after

1...♖xa7 2.♖h7+ The skewer!

2...♔e6 3.♖xa7+−

Try to obtain a decisive material advantage in each position by using a skewer!

PUZZLE 1

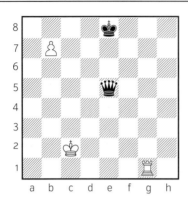

1. +−

PUZZLE 2

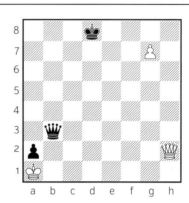

1. +−

PUZZLE 3

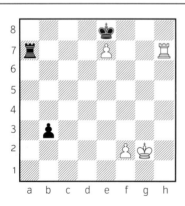

1. +−

PUZZLE 4

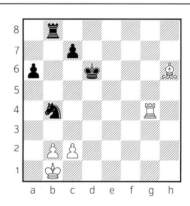

1. +−

PUZZLE 5

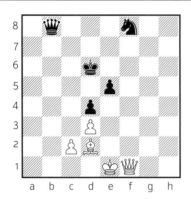

1. +–

PUZZLE 6

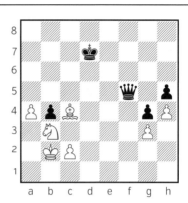

1. +–

PUZZLE 7

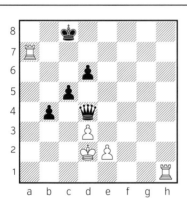

1. +–

PUZZLE 8

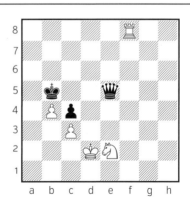

1. +–

PUZZLE 9

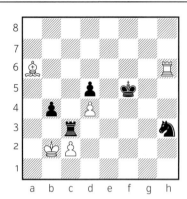

1. +–

PUZZLE 10

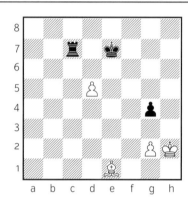

1. +–

PUZZLE 11

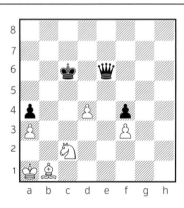

1. +–

PUZZLE 12

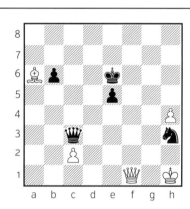

1. +–

PUZZLE 13

PUZZLE 14

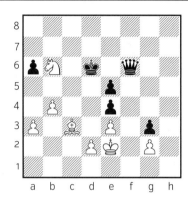

1. +–

1. +–

PUZZLE 15

PUZZLE 16

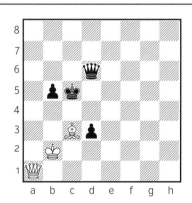

1. +–

1. +–

PUZZLE 17

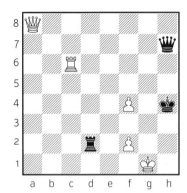

1. +–

PUZZLE 18

1. +–

PUZZLE 19

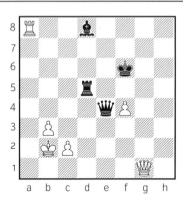

1. +–

PUZZLE 20

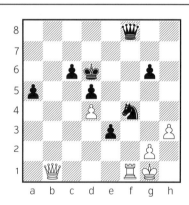

1. +–

PUZZLE 21

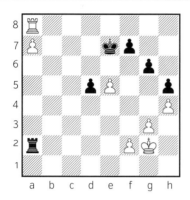

1. +–

PUZZLE 22

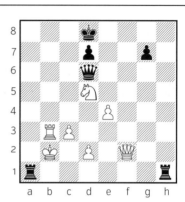

1. +–

PUZZLE 23

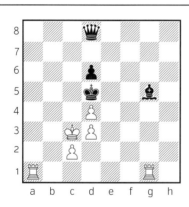

1. +–

PUZZLE 24

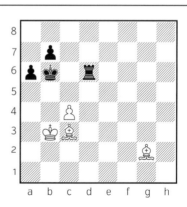

1. +–

PUZZLE 25

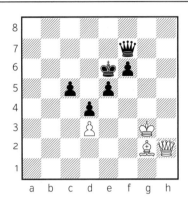

1. +–

PUZZLE 26

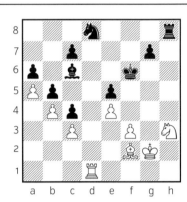

1. +–

PUZZLE 27

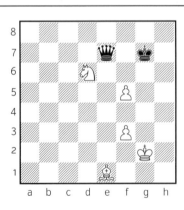

1. +–

PUZZLE 28

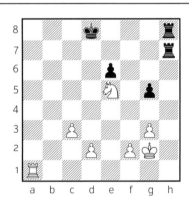

1. +–

PUZZLE 29

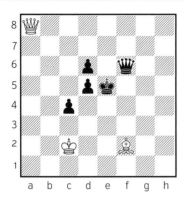

1. +– ....

....

PUZZLE 30

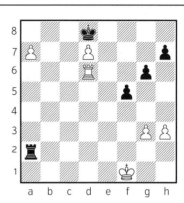

1. +– ....

....

PUZZLE 31

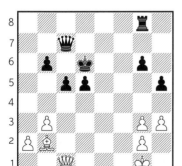

1. +– ....

....

PUZZLE 32

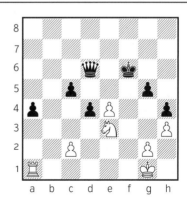

1. +– ....

....

PUZZLE 33

1. +−

PUZZLE 34

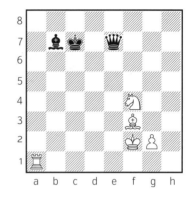

1. +−

PUZZLE 35

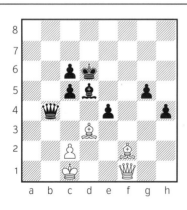

1. +−

PUZZLE 36

1. +−

PUZZLE 37

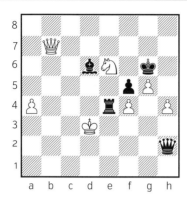

1. +−

PUZZLE 38

1. +−

PUZZLE 39

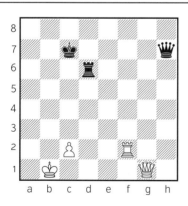

1. +−

PUZZLE 40

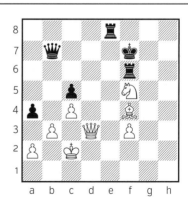

1. +−

CHAPTER 10.
DOUBLE ATTACK

Example 1	Example 2

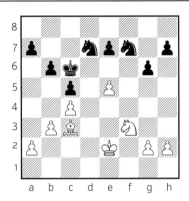

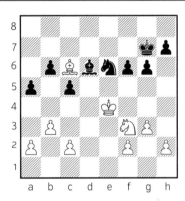

The double attack is one of the most important motifs in chess. A double attack is so-called because we attack two of our opponents' pieces in only one move!

1.e6

The pawn moves forward and attacks both knights, creating a double-attack, so White wins material. This kind of double attack is also called a "fork" as the pawn creates a fork shape by threatening to take in both directions.

1...♘d6 2.exd7+–

Double attacks can be executed by all the pieces. Sometimes it is even possible with the king. For example in this position White plays

1.♔d5

The king double attacks the knight and the bishop and one of the pieces must be lost.

1...♔f7 2.♔xd6+–

In this chapter, you will need to find a lot of hidden double attacks to win material.

PUZZLE 1

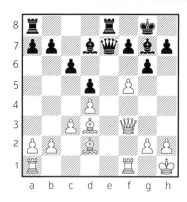

1. +–

PUZZLE 2

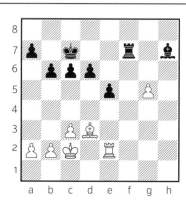

1. +–

PUZZLE 3

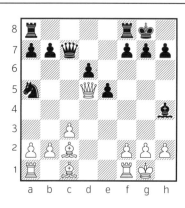

1. +–

PUZZLE 4

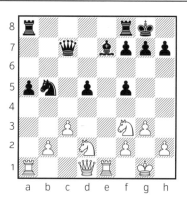

1. +–

PUZZLE 5

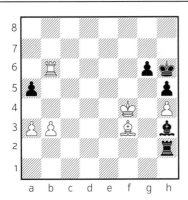

1. +–

PUZZLE 6

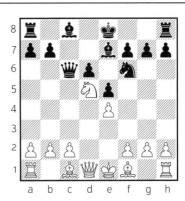

1. +–

PUZZLE 7

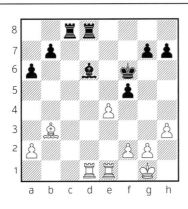

1. +–

PUZZLE 8

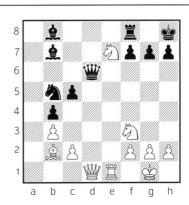

1. +–

PUZZLE 9

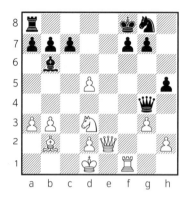

1. +−

PUZZLE 10

1. +−

PUZZLE 11

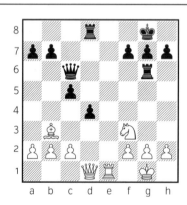

1. +−

PUZZLE 12

1. +−

PUZZLE 13

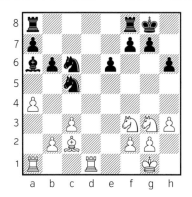

1. +– ....

....

PUZZLE 14

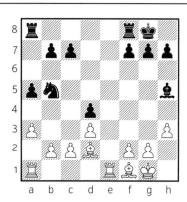

1. +– ....

....

PUZZLE 15

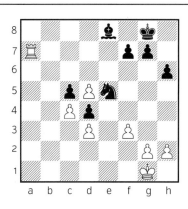

1. +– ....

....

PUZZLE 16

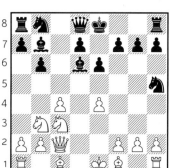

1. +– ....

....

PUZZLE 17

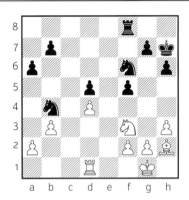

1. +−

PUZZLE 18

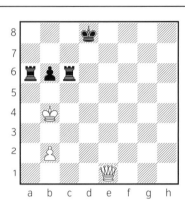

1. +−

PUZZLE 19

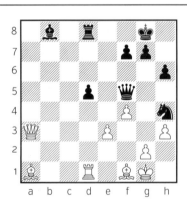

1. +−

PUZZLE 20

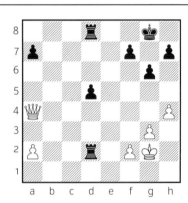

1. +−

PUZZLE 21

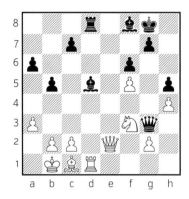

1. +–

PUZZLE 22

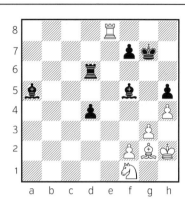

1. +–

PUZZLE 23

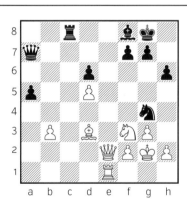

1. +–

PUZZLE 24

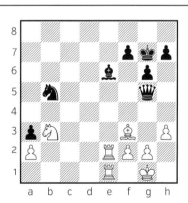

1. +–

PUZZLE 25

PUZZLE 26

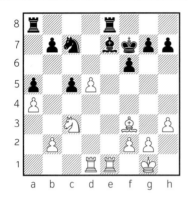

1. +−

1. +−

PUZZLE 27

PUZZLE 28

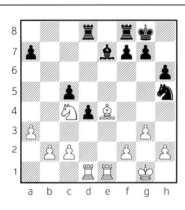

1. +−

1. +−

PUZZLE 29

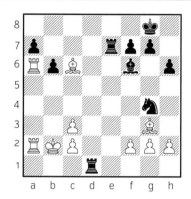

1. +–

PUZZLE 30

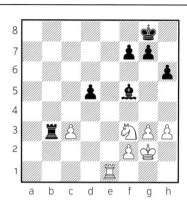

1. +–

PUZZLE 31

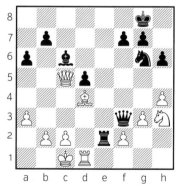

1. +–

PUZZLE 32

1. +–

PUZZLE 33

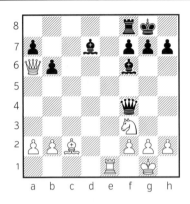

1. +–

PUZZLE 34

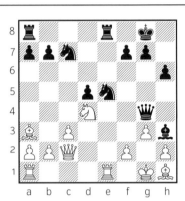

1. +–

PUZZLE 35

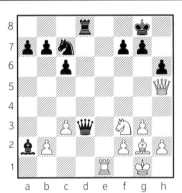

1. +–

PUZZLE 36

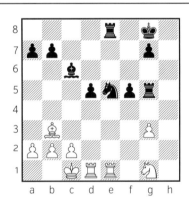

1. +–

PUZZLE 37

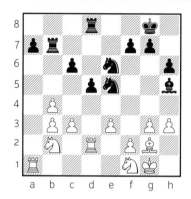

1. +— ....

....

PUZZLE 38

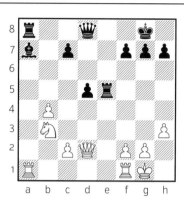

1. +— ....

....

PUZZLE 39

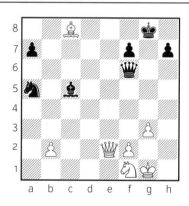

1. +— ....

....

PUZZLE 40

1. +— ....

....

TESTS

Dear Reader, We hope you have successfully mastered all the topics we covered in this book. You have now arrived at the test section, where you can test your knowledge over 8 tests.

Each test contains 10 exercises, one from each topic we covered earlier in this book. We suggest you first try to solve the test fully, and then check your solutions at the end of the book.

TEST #1

PUZZLE 1

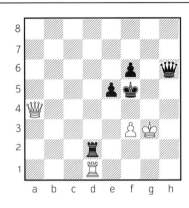

1. +– ....

....

PUZZLE 2

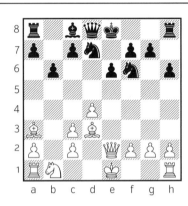

1. +– ....

....

PUZZLE 3

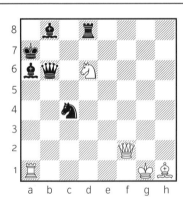

1. +– ....

....

PUZZLE 4

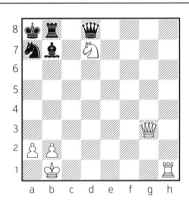

1. +– ....

....

PUZZLE 5

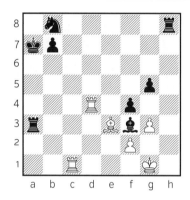

1. +–
....

....

PUZZLE 6

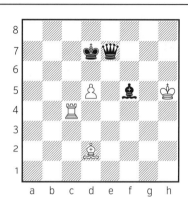

1. =
....

....

PUZZLE 7

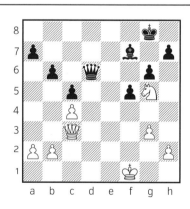

1. +–
....

....

PUZZLE 8

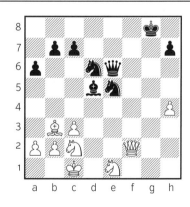

1. +–
....

....

PUZZLE 9

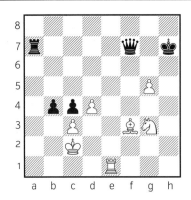

1. +–

PUZZLE 10

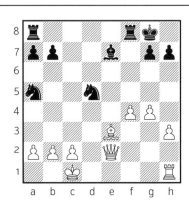

1. +–

TEST #2

PUZZLE 1

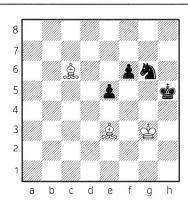

1. +−

PUZZLE 2

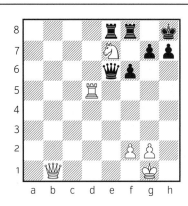

1. +−

PUZZLE 3

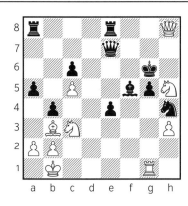

1. +−

PUZZLE 4

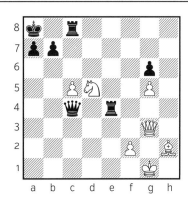

1. +−

PUZZLE 5

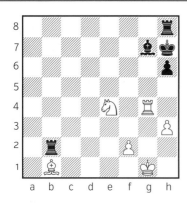

1. +−

PUZZLE 6

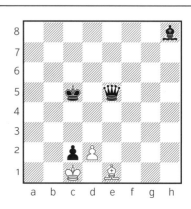

1. =

PUZZLE 7

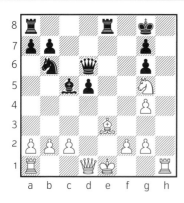

1. +−

PUZZLE 8

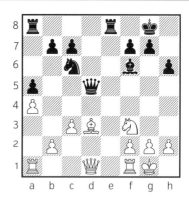

1. +−

PUZZLE 9

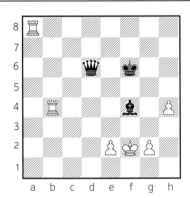

1. +−
···

···

PUZZLE 10

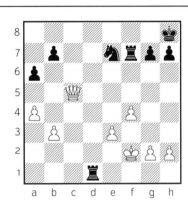

1. +−
···

···

TEST #3

PUZZLE 1

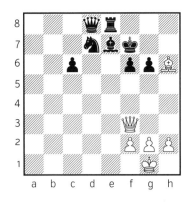

1. +–
....

....

PUZZLE 2

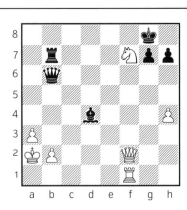

1. +–
....

....

PUZZLE 3

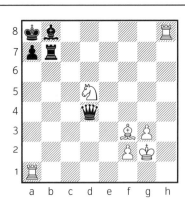

1. +–
....

....

PUZZLE 4

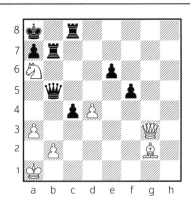

1. +–
....

....

PUZZLE 5

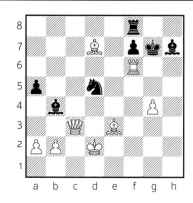

1. +−

PUZZLE 6

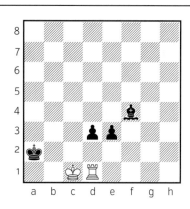

1. =

PUZZLE 7

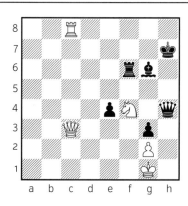

1. +−

PUZZLE 8

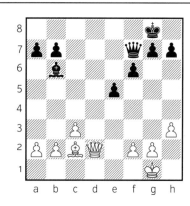

1. +−

PUZZLE 9

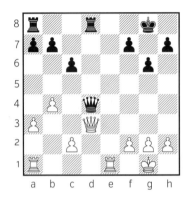

1. +−

PUZZLE 10

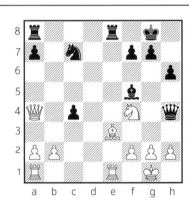

1. +−

TEST #4

PUZZLE 1

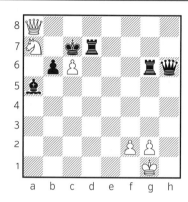

1. +–

....

....

PUZZLE 2

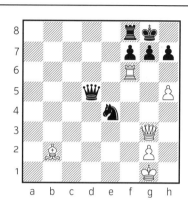

1. +–

....

....

PUZZLE 3

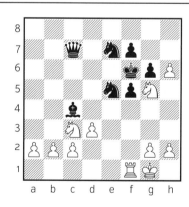

1. +–

....

....

PUZZLE 4

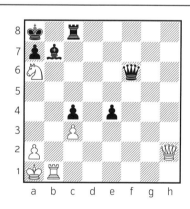

1. +–

....

....

PUZZLE 5

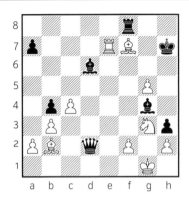

1. +−

PUZZLE 6

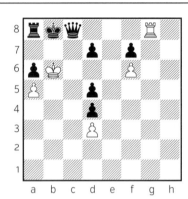

1. =

PUZZLE 7

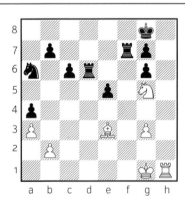

1. +−

PUZZLE 8

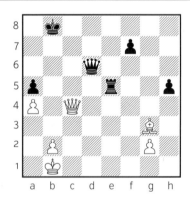

1. +−

PUZZLE 9

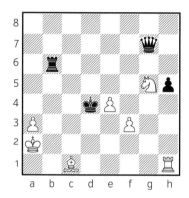

1. +−

PUZZLE 10

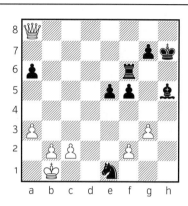

1. +−

TEST #5

PUZZLE 1

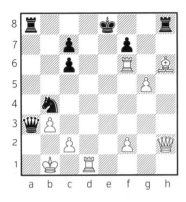

1. +– ....

....

PUZZLE 2

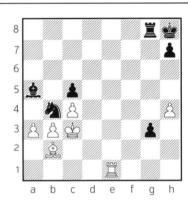

1. +– ....

....

PUZZLE 3

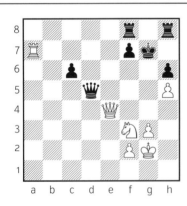

1. +– ....

....

PUZZLE 4

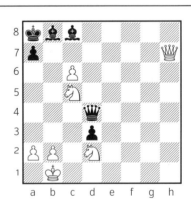

1. +– ....

....

PUZZLE 5

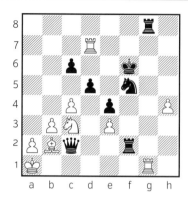

1. +–

PUZZLE 6

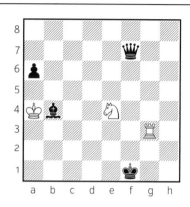

1. =

PUZZLE 7

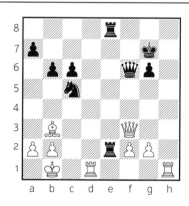

1. +–

PUZZLE 8

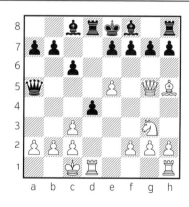

1. +–

PUZZLE 9

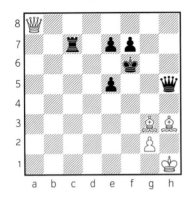

1. +–

....

....

PUZZLE 10

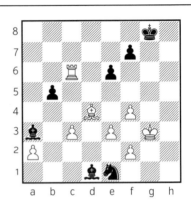

1. +–

....

....

TEST #6

PUZZLE 1

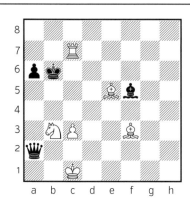

1. +–
....

....

PUZZLE 2

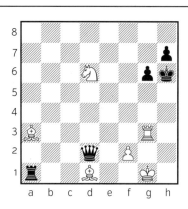

1. +–
....

....

PUZZLE 3

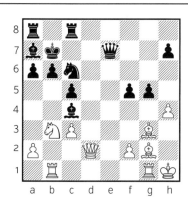

1. +–
....

....

PUZZLE 4

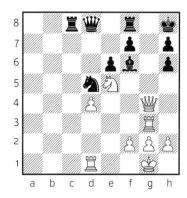

1. +–
....

....

PUZZLE 5

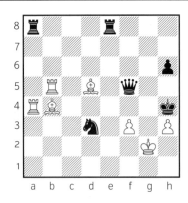

1. +–

PUZZLE 6

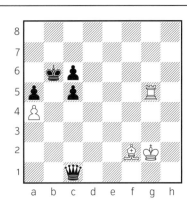

1. =

PUZZLE 7

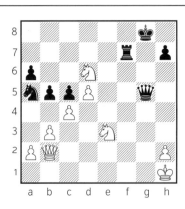

1. +–

PUZZLE 8

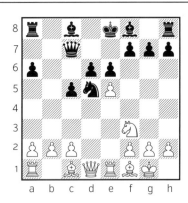

1. +–

PUZZLE 9

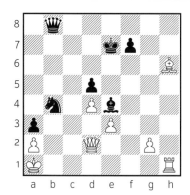

1. +−

....

....

PUZZLE 10

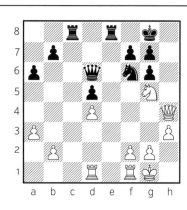

1. +−

....

....

TEST #7

PUZZLE 1

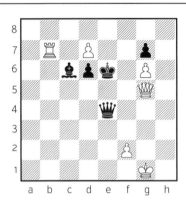

1. +−

....

....

PUZZLE 2

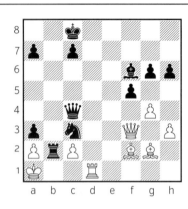

1. +−

....

....

PUZZLE 3

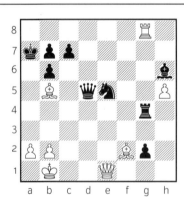

1. +−

....

....

PUZZLE 4

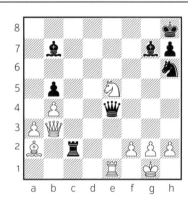

1. +−

....

....

PUZZLE 5

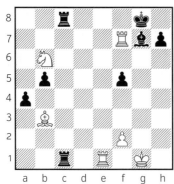

1. +−

....

....

PUZZLE 6

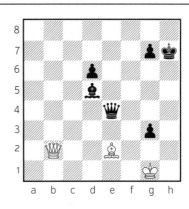

1. =

....

....

PUZZLE 7

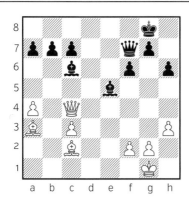

1. +−

....

....

PUZZLE 8

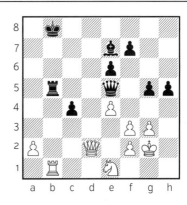

1. +−

....

....

PUZZLE 9

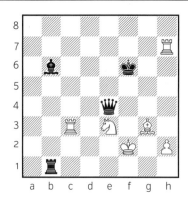

1. +–

PUZZLE 10

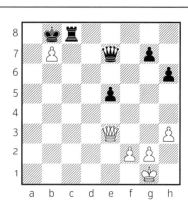

1. +–

TEST #8

PUZZLE 1

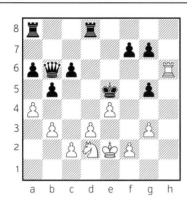

1. +–

PUZZLE 2

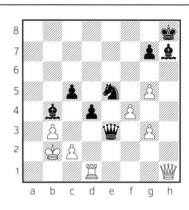

1. +–

PUZZLE 3

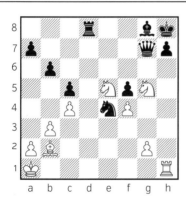

1. +–

PUZZLE 4

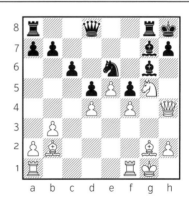

1. +–

PUZZLE 5

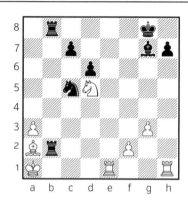

1. +−

PUZZLE 6

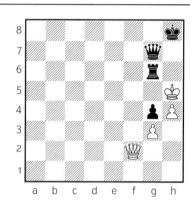

1. =

PUZZLE 7

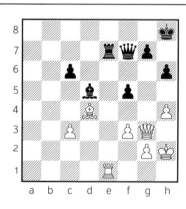

1. +−

PUZZLE 8

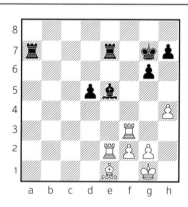

1. +−

PUZZLE 9

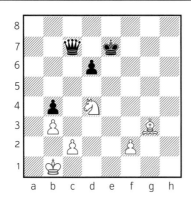

1. +−
....

....

PUZZLE 10

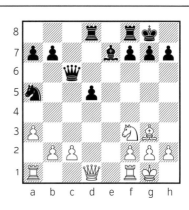

1. +−
....

....

SOLUTIONS

Chapter 1

■ **Puzzle 1**

1.♖b8#

■ **Puzzle 2**

1.♗e5#

■ **Puzzle 3**

1.♗c6#

■ **Puzzle 4**

1.♘f7#

■ **Puzzle 5**

1.♖ag7#

■ **Puzzle 6**

1.♕f8#

■ **Puzzle 7**

1.♖e8#

■ **Puzzle 8**

1.♗e5#

■ **Puzzle 9**

1.♘g3#

■ **Puzzle 10**

1.♕g6#

■ **Puzzle 11**

1.♕d8#

■ **Puzzle 12**

1.♖h7#

■ Puzzle 13

1. ♖h5#

■ Puzzle 14

1. ♘h6#

■ Puzzle 15

1. ♖f7#

■ Puzzle 16

1. ♗f6#

■ Puzzle 17

1. ♘h6#

■ Puzzle 18

1. ♕h7#

■ Puzzle 19

1. ♗e4#

■ Puzzle 20

1. 0−0#

■ Puzzle 21

1. c8N#

■ Puzzle 22

1. ♗g7#

■ Puzzle 23

1. ♘h6#

■ Puzzle 24

1. ♕c6#

■ Puzzle 25

1. ♗f7#

■ Puzzle 26

1. ♗b3#

■ Puzzle 27

1. ♗c3#

■ Puzzle 28

1. ♗c7#

■ **Puzzle 29**

1.♕h8#

■ **Puzzle 30**

1.♘g1#

■ **Puzzle 31**

1.♖h8#

■ **Puzzle 32**

1.f5#

■ **Puzzle 33**

1.♘a7#

■ **Puzzle 34**

1.♘e7#

■ **Puzzle 35**

1.♘f4#

■ **Puzzle 36**

1.♕g8#

■ **Puzzle 37**

1.♗b8#

■ **Puzzle 38**

1.a4#

■ **Puzzle 39**

1.h4#

■ **Puzzle 40**

1.♘c5#

Chapter 2

■ **Puzzle 1**

1.♕xg7+ ♖xg7 2.♖f8#

■ **Puzzle 2**

1.♕g8+ ♘xg8 2.♗f5#

■ Puzzle 3

1.♖xh7+ ♔xh7 2.♕h5#

■ Puzzle 4

1.♘f6+ gxf6 [1...♔h8 2.♖xf8#]

2.♖xf8#

■ Puzzle 5

1.♕xh6+ ♗xh6 [1...♔g8 2.♕xg7#]

2.♖xh6#

■ Puzzle 6

1.♕b8+ ♘xb8 2.♖d8#

■ Puzzle 7

1.♖h6+ gxh6 2.♖h7#

■ Puzzle 8

1.♖e8+ ♕xe8 2.♘f6#

■ Puzzle 9

1.♕xh6+ gxh6 2.♖h7#

■ Puzzle 10

1.♕xh7+ ♔xh7 2.♖h3#

■ Puzzle 11

1.♕xh6+ ♔xh6 2.♖h8#

■ Puzzle 12

1.♕f8+ ♔xf8 [1...♔h7 2.♕g7#]

2.♖d8#

■ Puzzle 13

1.♖c8+ ♗xc8 [1...♗e8 2.♖cxe8#]

2.♖e8#

■ Puzzle 14

1.♖f6+ ♔xf6 2.♖d6#

■ Puzzle 15

1.♕xf8+ ♔xf8 2.♖e8#

■ Puzzle 16

1.♕xg4+ fxg4 2.♖xg4#

■ Puzzle 17

1.♕xh5+ ♔xh5 2.♖h4#

■ Puzzle 18

1.♖e8+ ♗xe8 2.♖d8#

■ Puzzle 19

1.♕xh6+ gxh6 2.♖xh6#

■ Puzzle 20

1.♕f6+ ♗xf6 2.♗xf6#

■ Puzzle 21

1.♘g6+ hxg6 2.♖h4#

■ Puzzle 22

1.♕xf8+ ♔xf8 [1...♔h7 2.♕xg7#]

2.♖d8#

■ Puzzle 23

1.♖xf8+ ♔xf8 2.♕d8#

■ Puzzle 24

1.♕xh7+ ♔xh7 2.♖h5#

■ Puzzle 25

1.♘e5+ ♔b6 2.♗d8#

■ Puzzle 26

1.♗g7+ ♔g8 2.♘h6#

■ Puzzle 27

1.e6+ ♔g8 2.e7#

■ Puzzle 28

1.♘c6+ bxc6 2.♗b8#

■ Puzzle 29

1.♕xf6+ exf6 2.♗xf6#

■ Puzzle 30

1.g7+ ♔xg7 [1...♔e8 2.g8♕#]

2.♕h6#

■ Puzzle 31

1.♖b8+ ♗xb8 2.♖f8#

■ Puzzle 32

1.♕b5+ cxb5 [1...♔a8 2.♕b7#]

2.♘a6#

■ Puzzle 33

1.♕xc7+ ♗xc7 2.♖b7#

■ Puzzle 34

1.♗xg7+ ♔xg7 2.♕f6#

■ Puzzle 35

1.♖xa6+ ♔xa6 [1...bxa6 2.♕b8#]

2.♕a8#

■ Puzzle 36

1.♕a8+ ♖xa8 2.♖xa8#

■ Puzzle 37

1.e8♕+ ♘xe8 [1...♔h7 2.♕gg6#]

2.♕g8#

■ Puzzle 38

1.♖a6+ bxa6 2.♕a5#

■ Puzzle 39

1.♖xh7+ ♔xh7 2.♕h1#

■ Puzzle 40

1.♖xa7+ ♔xa7 2.♕a5#

Chapter 3

■ Puzzle 1

1.♘g6#

■ Puzzle 2

1.♖h6#

■ Puzzle 3

1.♖a6#

■ Puzzle 4

1.♕g5#

■ Puzzle 5

1.♕f5#

■ Puzzle 6

1.♖a6#

■ Puzzle 7

1.♘c6#

■ Puzzle 8

1.♖a5#

■ Puzzle 9

1.♖b6#

■ Puzzle 10

1.♘f5#

■ Puzzle 11

1.♖h5#

■ Puzzle 12

1.♘b4#

■ Puzzle 13

1.♕h3#

■ Puzzle 14

1.♕g8#

■ Puzzle 15

1.♕xh5#

■ Puzzle 16

1.♕g7#

■ Puzzle 17

1.♕xc7#

■ Puzzle 18

1.♕f8#

■ Puzzle 19

1.♕xf7#

■ Puzzle 20

1.♘d5#

■ Puzzle 21

1.♕xf7#

■ Puzzle 22

1.♗e4#

■ Puzzle 23

1.♖h7#

■ Puzzle 24

1.♕c5#

■ Puzzle 25

1.♖e8#

■ Puzzle 26

1.♘g5#

■ Puzzle 27

1.♘e7#

■ Puzzle 28

1.♘f6#

■ Puzzle 29

1.♕a8#

■ Puzzle 30

1.♕e7#

■ Puzzle 31

1.♘d6#

■ Puzzle 32

1.♘f7#

■ Puzzle 33

1.♖g8#

■ Puzzle 34

1.♘e5#

■ **Puzzle 35**

1.♘c7#

■ **Puzzle 36**

1.♕e8#

■ **Puzzle 37**

1.♕xg6#

■ **Puzzle 38**

1.♕a7#

■ **Puzzle 39**

1.♕f5#

■ **Puzzle 40**

1.d4#

Chapter 4

■ **Puzzle 1**

1.♖h5+ gxh5 2.g5#

■ **Puzzle 2**

1.♕xh7+ ♕xh7 2.♘f7#

■ **Puzzle 3**

1.♖b8+ ♖xb8 2.♘c7#

■ **Puzzle 4**

1.♗d4+ ♗g7 2.♘f7#

■ **Puzzle 5**

1.♖xg7+ ♕xg7 2.♘f6#

■ **Puzzle 6**

1.g7+ ♘xg7 2.♘g6#

■ **Puzzle 7**

1.♔f4 g3 2.hxg3#

■ **Puzzle 8**

1.♘g6+ ♔g8 2.♗e6#

■ Puzzle 9

1.♕xh7+ ♖xh7 2.♘g6#

■ Puzzle 10

1.♖c3+ dxc3 2.d3#

■ Puzzle 11

1.♕xg7+ ♖xg7 2.hxg7#

■ Puzzle 12

1.♕g8+ ♖xg8 2.♘f7#

■ Puzzle 13

1.♖xh7+ ♘xh7 2.♘f7#

■ Puzzle 14

1.♕xg7+ ♘xg7 2.♘h6#

■ Puzzle 15

1.♖e7+ ♗xe7 2.f7#

■ Puzzle 16

1.♖xb7+ ♘xb7 2.♘a6#

■ Puzzle 17

1.♖g8+ ♖xg8 2.♘f7#

■ Puzzle 18

1.♕xh7+ ♘xh7 2.g7#

■ Puzzle 19

1.♕g8+ ♕xg8 2.♘g6#

■ Puzzle 20

1.♘d6+ ♔a8 2.b7#

■ Puzzle 21

1.♘f5+ ♔h8 2.g7#

■ Puzzle 22

1.♕h8+ ♗xh8 2.♘f8#

■ Puzzle 23

1.♕c7+ ♖xc7 2.bxc7#

■ Puzzle 24

1.♕e7+ ♗xe7 2.♘f7#

■ Puzzle 25

1.♖xa7+ ♗xa7 2.♘c7#

■ Puzzle 26

1.♕xg7+ ♕xg7 2.♘g6#

■ Puzzle 27

1.♖b8+ ♖xb8 2.♘c7#

■ Puzzle 28

1.♖c8+ ♘b8 2.♘c7#

■ Puzzle 29

1.♕xa7+ ♗xa7 2.♘b6#

■ Puzzle 30

1.♕b7+ ♗xb7 2.cxb7#

■ Puzzle 31

1.♘e7+ ♔h8 2.♘f7#

■ Puzzle 32

1.♖d8+ ♖b8 2.♗g2#

■ Puzzle 33

1.♖f8+ ♖g8 2.b3#

■ Puzzle 34

1.♘f7+ ♔g8 2.♘5h6#

■ Puzzle 35

1.♘b6+ ♔b8 2.♘ed7#

■ Puzzle 36

1.♖a3+ bxa3 2.b3#

■ Puzzle 37

1.♕h5+ ♖h6 2.g6#

■ Puzzle 38

1.c8♘+ ♔a8 2.♘4b6#

■ Puzzle 39

1.♘h6+ ♔h8 2.♘g6#

■ Puzzle 40

1.♖xh7+ ♗xh7 2.♘g6#

Chapter 5

■ Puzzle 1

1.♗e3#

■ Puzzle 2

1.♘xf7#

■ Puzzle 3

1.♗b5#

■ Puzzle 4

1.♘e7#

■ Puzzle 5

1.♘c7#

■ Puzzle 6

1.♘e6#

■ Puzzle 7

1.♘c6#

■ Puzzle 8

1.c8♘#

■ Puzzle 9

1.♖xg6#

■ Puzzle 10

1.♗xd6#

■ Puzzle 11

1.♖f8#

■ Puzzle 12

1.♖g6#

■ Puzzle 13

1.♖e8#

■ Puzzle 14

1.♘d6#

■ Puzzle 15

1.♘d6#

■ Puzzle 16

1.♗e6#

■ Puzzle 17

1.♘f6#

■ Puzzle 18

1.♘f5#

■ Puzzle 19

1.♗a5+ ♔e8 2.♖d8#

■ Puzzle 20

1.♗e8+ ♔h6 2.♖h5#

■ Puzzle 21

1.♘f6+ ♔d8 [1...♔f8 2.♖e8#]

2.♖e8#

■ Puzzle 22

1.♘f7+ ♔g8 2.♘h6#

■ Puzzle 23

1.♘d7+ ♔a8 2.♘b6#

■ Puzzle 24

1.♗g5+ ♔c7 [1...♔e8 2.♖d8#]

2.♗d8#

■ Puzzle 25

1.♘c6+ ♔a8 2.♕a7#

■ Puzzle 26

1.♘c8+ ♔a8 2.♖a7#

■ Puzzle 27

1.♘f7+ ♔g8 2.♖h8#

■ Puzzle 28

1.♘f5+ ♔g8 2.♘e7#

■ **Puzzle 29**

1.♘b5+ ♔a6 [1...♔b8 2.♖d8#]

2.♘c7#

■ **Puzzle 30**

1.♘c4+ ♔a6 [1...♔a4 2.♖a5#]

2.♖a5#

■ **Puzzle 31**

1.c8N+ ♔a8 2.♖a7#

■ **Puzzle 32**

1.♘f6+ ♔f8 [1...♔d8 2.♖e8#]

2.♘d7#

■ **Puzzle 33**

1.♖g3+ ♔h6 2.♗g7#

■ **Puzzle 34**

1.♖g5+ ♔h7 2.♕g7#

■ **Puzzle 35**

1.♖b6+ ♔a8 2.♖b8#

■ **Puzzle 36**

1.♖h5+ ♔g8 2.♖h8#

■ **Puzzle 37**

1.♗f6+ ♔c7 [1...♔e8 2.♖d8#]

2.♗d8#

■ **Puzzle 38**

1.e8♕+ ♔xe8 2.♖h8#

■ **Puzzle 39**

1.♘d8+ ♔c8 [1...♔a6 2.♖a1#]

2.♗b7#

■ **Puzzle 40**

1.f8N+ ♔h6 [1...♔h8 2.♘g6#]

2.♖h7#

Chapter 6

■ **Puzzle 1**

1.♖f1+ ♚xf1=

■ **Puzzle 2**

1.♕f3+ ♕xf3=

■ **Puzzle 3**

1.♖e8+ ♖xe8=

■ **Puzzle 4**

1.♖b1 ♖xb1=

■ **Puzzle 5**

1.♕g6+ ♕xg6=

■ **Puzzle 6**

1.♕g5+ ♚xg5= [1...♕xg5=]

■ **Puzzle 7**

1.♖a4+ ♕xa4=

■ **Puzzle 8**

1.f8♕+ ♕xf8=

■ **Puzzle 9**

1.♖d4 ♗xd4=

■ **Puzzle 10**

1.♔c3 ♗xg8=

■ **Puzzle 11**

1.♖xd6+ ♕xd6= [1...♔g5 2.♖xd1=]

■ **Puzzle 12**

1.e8♕+ ♖xe8=

■ **Puzzle 13**

1.♖b1 ♕xb1=

■ **Puzzle 14**

1.♖xd6+ ♕xd6= [1...♔g5 2.♖xd1=]

■ Puzzle 15

1.♕f2 ♕xf2=

■ Puzzle 16

1.c7 ♔xc7= [1...♗xc7=]

■ Puzzle 17

1.b4 ♕xd4=

■ Puzzle 18

1.♕h7+ ♔xh7=

■ Puzzle 19

1.♕h6+ ♔xh6=

■ Puzzle 20

1.♖g4+ ♕xg4 2.♘e3+ ♗xe3= [2...♔f3 3.♘xg4=]

■ Puzzle 21

1.c7+ ♔xb7 2.c8♕+ ♔xc8= [2... ♗xc8=]

■ Puzzle 22

1.h6 ♖a8+ [1...♕xc3=]

2.♔b1 ♕xc3=

■ Puzzle 23

1.a7+ ♔a8 2.♔a6 b1♕= [2...b1♖=]

■ Puzzle 24

1.♔f2+ g1♕+ [1...g1♖ 2.♖f1 ♖xf1+ 3.♔xf1=]

2.♔f3 ♕xe1=

■ Puzzle 25

1.d8♕ ♖d1+ 2.♔e3 ♖xd8=

■ Puzzle 26

1.♖f7+ ♔e8 2.♖f8+ ♔xf8=

■ Puzzle 27

1.♔g1 ♖g2+ 2.♔h1 ♖xg7= [2...♖g4 3.g8♕ ♖xg8=]

■ Puzzle 28

1.♗d4 g3 2.♗xf2 gxf2=

■ Puzzle 29

1.e7 ♖xf7 2.♔a6 ♖xe7=

■ Puzzle 30

1.h8♕ ♗xh8 2.♗g7 ♗xg7=

■ Puzzle 31

1.c7 ♕xc7 2.b8♕ ♕xb8=

■ Puzzle 32

1.♔a3 b1♕ 2.♘c3+ ♘xc3=

■ Puzzle 33

1.♗c3+ ♕xc3 2.♖g8+ ♔xg8=

■ Puzzle 34

1.♖b3+ ♔c4 2.♖c3+ ♔d5 3.♖d3 ♕xd3=

■ Puzzle 35

1.♖e8+ ♗xe8 2.♘e7+ ♔f8 3.♘g6+ hxg6= [3...♔g8 4.♘e7+=; 3...fxg6=]

■ Puzzle 36

1.♔g3 a3 2.♔h4 a2 3.g3 a1♕ =

■ Puzzle 37

1.b3+ ♕xb3 [1...♔xb3 2.♘d2+ ♔c3 3.♘xc4=]

2.♘c5+ ♘xc5=

■ Puzzle 38

1.♖xh7+ ♔xh7 2.♕xg7+ ♔xg7

■ Puzzle 39

1.♗xd3 ♔xd3 2.♔c1 ♔c3= [2...a3=]

■ Puzzle 40

1.♕d4+ ♖6xd4= [1...♖1xd4=]

Chapter 7

■ **Puzzle 1**

1.♘xc7+ ♗xc7 2.♕xc6++−

■ **Puzzle 2**

1.♖g5+ hxg5 2.♕xd6+−

■ **Puzzle 3**

1.♖e8+ ♔g7 [1...♖xe8 2.♕xf6+−]

2.♖g8+ [2.♕xf6+ ♔xf6 3.♖xe2+−]

2...♔xg8 3.♕xf6+−

■ **Puzzle 4**

1.♘c5+ bxc5 2.♘a5+ ♔c8 3.♘xc6+−

■ **Puzzle 5**

1.♕xg7+ ♔xg7 2.♘e8+ ♔g6 3.♘xd6+−

■ **Puzzle 6**

1.♕g8+ ♔xg8 2.♘xe7+ ♔f7 3.♘xc8+−

■ **Puzzle 7**

1.♖xd8 ♔xd8 2.♗xb6+ ♔d7 3.♗xa5+−

■ **Puzzle 8**

1.♖xb6+ axb6 2.♖xb6++−

■ **Puzzle 9**

1.♖xc8+ ♔xc8 2.♕xb6+−

■ **Puzzle 10**

1.♖xh6+ ♗xh6 2.♕xb2++−

■ **Puzzle 11**

1.♘f6+ ♗xf6 2.♕xd7+−

■ **Puzzle 12**

1.♕f8+ ♔xf8 2.♘xd7+ ♔e8 3.♘xe5+−

■ **Puzzle 13**

1.♕xc6 ♕xc6 2.♘xe7+ ♔h8 3.♘xc6+−

■ Puzzle 14

1.♗xf7+ ♔xf7 2.♕xd8+−

■ Puzzle 15

1.♖a7+ ♔xa7 2.♕xc6+−

■ Puzzle 16

1.♖h8+ ♔xh8 2.♘xf7+ ♔g8
3.♘xg5+−

■ Puzzle 17

1.♘xf7+ ♖xf7 2.♕xd8++−

■ Puzzle 18

1.♗xd4 ♕xd4 2.♘xf5+ ♔g8
3.♘xd4+−

■ Puzzle 19

1.♖xd7+ ♕xd7 2.♘xe5+ ♔e8
3.♘xd7+−

■ Puzzle 20

1.♗xf7+ ♔xf7 2.♘g5+ ♔e8 [2...♔f6
3.♕f3#] 3.♘e6+−

■ Puzzle 21

1.♕xg6+ ♔xg6 2.♘e5+ ♔g7
3.♘xd7+−

■ Puzzle 22

1.♖xd6 cxd6 2.♕xc4+ ♕f7 [2...♔h8
3.♕xa2+−]

3.♗d5+−

■ Puzzle 23

1.♗xf7+ ♔xf7 [1...♕xf7 2.♘xd6+
♔f8 3.♘xf7+−]

2.♘g5+ ♔e8 3.♘xe6+−

■ Puzzle 24

1.♖f8+ ♖xf8 [1...♘xf8 2.♕xg7#]

2.♕xe6++−

■ Puzzle 25

1.♖xd7 ♕xd7 2.♘xf6+ ♔g7
3.♘xd7+−

■ Puzzle 26

1.♖xf8+ ♔xf8 2.♕xd7+−

■ Puzzle 27

1.♖xh7+ ♔xh7 2.♘xf6+ ♔h8
3.♘xg4+−

■ Puzzle 28

1.♘xe6+ ♗xe6 2.♕xb4++−

■ Puzzle 29

1.♗h7+ ♔xh7 2.♕xc5+−

■ Puzzle 30

1.♖d8+ ♔xd8 2.♕xc6+−

■ Puzzle 31

1.♖xf6 ♕xf6 2.♗xe5+−

■ Puzzle 32

1.♖xe3 ♕xe2 [1...dxe3 2.♕xg4+−]
2.♖xe2+−

■ Puzzle 33

1.♘e7+ ♖xe7 2.♕xc8++−

■ Puzzle 34

1.♕xd7+ ♔xd7 2.dxc5+ ♔c6 3.cxb6+−

■ Puzzle 35

1.♗xa7+ ♔xa7 2.♕xh3+−

■ Puzzle 36

1.♖c8+ ♖xc8 2.♕xb2+−

■ Puzzle 37

1.♖xd3 exd3 2.♗d5+−

■ Puzzle 38

1.♕xe5 dxe5 2.♖xd7+−

■ Puzzle 39

1.e8♕ ♖xe8 2.♖xg7+−

■ Puzzle 40

1.♖e8+ ♔xe8 [1...♔f7 2.♘d6+ ♔g6
3.♘xf5+−] 2.♘d6+ ♔e7 3.♘xf5++−

Chapter 8

■ **Puzzle 1**

1.♗e8 ♕xe8 2.♖xe8+−

■ **Puzzle 2**

1.♗h5 0–0 2.♗xg6+−

■ **Puzzle 3**

1.♗a5 ♔d7 2.♗xb6+−

■ **Puzzle 4**

1.♘d4+ ♔c5 2.♘xc6+−

■ **Puzzle 5**

1.♖f8+ ♘xf8 2.♕xg4+−

■ **Puzzle 6**

1.♖d1 ♕xc3 2.♖xd7+ ♔f6 3.bxc3+−

■ **Puzzle 7**

1.♖b8 ♖xb8 2.♗xe5+ ♔g8 3.♗xb8+−

■ **Puzzle 8**

1.♗b5 0–0 2.♗xd7+−

■ **Puzzle 9**

1.♖g4 ♕xg4 2.hxg4+−

■ **Puzzle 10**

1.♖h4 ♕xh4 2.♗xh4+−

■ **Puzzle 11**

1.♖a8 ♕xa8 2.♗xa8+−

■ **Puzzle 12**

1.♘h6+ ♔h8 2.♘xf7++−

■ **Puzzle 13**

1.♘a6 ♕c8 2.♘xc5+−

■ **Puzzle 14**

1.♘b6+ ♔b8 2.♘xd7++−

■ Puzzle 15

1.♘c6+ dxc6 2.♕xg7+–`

■ Puzzle 16

1.♗a7+ ♔xa7 2.♖xc4+–

■ Puzzle 17

1.♖a7 ♗e4 2.♖xg7++–

■ Puzzle 18

1.♗c5 ♗b6 2.♕f4+ ♔e8 3.♕xd6+–

■ Puzzle 19

1.♕h5+ ♔e7 2.♕xf3+–

■ Puzzle 20

1.♖c1 ♕xb3 2.♖xc8+ ♔f7 3.axb3+–

■ Puzzle 21

1.♕xg7+ ♔xg7 [1...♕xg7 2.gxf3+–]

2.gxf3+–

■ Puzzle 22

1.♘f4+ ♔g4 2.♘xh3+–

■ Puzzle 23

1.♖xd5 ♖xd5 2.♗c4 c6 3.e4+–

■ Puzzle 24

1.♖xe5 ♕xe5 2.♗g3+–

■ Puzzle 25

1.♕h5+ ♔f8 2.♖xe5+–

■ Puzzle 26

1.♘f6+ gxf6 2.♖xe8+–

■ Puzzle 27

1.♖xg5+ ♕xg5 2.♖g3 ♕xg3 3.fxg3+–

■ Puzzle 28

1.♕f3+ ♔h6 2.♖xd5+–

■ Puzzle 29

1.♕f6+ ♔g8 2.♗xe6++–

■ **Puzzle 30**

1.♖f3+ ♔d2 2.♖xc3+−

■ **Puzzle 31**

1.♘e4+ dxe4 2.♖xd2+−

■ **Puzzle 32**

1.♗h3 ♗xh3 2.♕xg6+−

■ **Puzzle 33**

1.♗xd6+ ♕xd6 2.♕xd6++−

■ **Puzzle 34**

1.♕xd5 ♕xd5 2.♗b3 ♕xb3 3.axb3+−

■ **Puzzle 35**

1.♗e4 ♗h7 2.♕f7+ ♔a6 3.♕xd5+−

■ **Puzzle 36**

1.♗f4 gxf4 2.♕xf4 ♕xg2 3.♕xe5++−

■ **Puzzle 37**

1.♘e6+ ♔e7 2.♘xf4+−

■ **Puzzle 38**

1.♖xg5+   ♕xg5   2.♖g1   ♕xg1
3.♕xg1++−

■ **Puzzle 39**

1.♖xe5 ♕xe5 [1...♖xe5 2.f4+−]

2.♖e1 ♕xc3 3.♖xe8+ ♔g7 4.bxc3+−

■ **Puzzle 40**

1.♕d4 ♖xa7 2.♕xd8+−

Chapter 9

■ **Puzzle 1**

1.b8♕+ ♕xb8 2.♖g8+ ♔d7 3.♖xb8+−

■ **Puzzle 2**

1.g8♕+ ♕xg8 2.♕b8+ ♔d7 3.♕xg8+−

■ Puzzle 3

1.♖h8+ ♔xe7 2.♖h7+ ♔d6 3.♖xa7 b2 4.♖b7+−

■ Puzzle 4

1.♖xb4 ♖xb4 2.♗f8+ ♔d5 3.♗xb4+−

■ Puzzle 5

1.♕xf8+ ♕xf8 2.♗b4+ ♔d5 3.♗xf8+−

■ Puzzle 6

1.♗e6+ ♕xe6 [1...♔xe6 2.♘d4+ ♔e5 3.♘xf5+−]

2.♘c5+ ♔d6 3.♘xe6+−

■ Puzzle 7

1.♖h8+ ♕xh8 2.♖a8+ ♔b7 3.♖xh8+−

■ Puzzle 8

1.♖f5 ♕xf5 2.♘d4+ ♔b6 3.♘xf5+−

■ Puzzle 9

1.♖xh3 ♖xh3 2.♗c8+ ♔e4 3.♗xh3+−

■ Puzzle 10

1.d6+ ♔xd6 2.♗g3+ ♔d7 3.♗xc7 ♔xc7 4.♗g3+−

■ Puzzle 11

1.d5+ ♔xd5 [1...♕xd5 2.♘b4+ ♔c5 3.♘xd5+−]

2.♗a2+ ♔e5 3.♗xe6+−

■ Puzzle 12

1.♗c8+ ♕xc8 [1...♔d6 2.♗xh3+−]

2.♕xh3+ ♔d5 3.♕xc8+−

■ Puzzle 13

1.♗xe5+ ♔xe5 [1...♕xe5 2.♘c4+ ♔e6 3.♘xe5+−]

2.♘d7+ ♔f5 3.♘xf6+−

■ Puzzle 14

1.♖xh7+ ♕xh7 2.♕h1+ ♔g5 3.♕xh7+−

■ Puzzle 15

1.♗b4+ ♔xb4 2.♕a3+ ♔c4 3.♕xd6+−

■ Puzzle 16

1.♖h4+ ♕xh4 2.♖a4+ ♔e5 3.♖xh4
e2 4.♖h1+–

■ Puzzle 17

1.♖h6+   ♕xh6   2.♕h1+   ♔g4
3.♕xh6+–

■ Puzzle 18

1.♗e5+ d6 2.♗xd6+ ♔xd6 3.♕h2+
♔d7 4.♕xb8+–

■ Puzzle 19

1.♖xd8 ♖xd8 2.♕g5+ ♔f7 3.♕xd8+–

■ Puzzle 20

1.♖xf4 ♕xf4 2.♕b8+ ♔e6 3.♕xf4+–

■ Puzzle 21

1.e6 fxe6 [1...♔xe6 2.♖e8+ ♔f6 3.a8♕
♖xa8 4.♖xa8+–; 1...d4 2.exf7 ♔xf7
3.♖h8 ♖xa7 4.♖h7+ ♔f6 5.♖xa7+–]

2.♖g8 ♖xa7 3.♖g7+ ♔d6 4.♖xa7+–

■ Puzzle 22

1.♕f8+ ♕xf8 2.♖b8#

■ Puzzle 23

1.♖xg5+ ♕xg5 2.♖a5+ ♔c6 3.♖xg5+–

■ Puzzle 24

1.c5+ ♔xc5 2.♗b4+ ♔d4 3.♗xd6+–

■ Puzzle 25

1.♗d5+ ♔xd5 2.♕a2+ ♔d6 3.♕xf7+–

■ Puzzle 26

1.♖xd8 ♖xd8 2.♗h4+ g5 3.♗xg5+
♔e6 4.♗xd8+–

■ Puzzle 27

1.f6+ ♔xf6 [1...♕xf6 2.♘e8+ ♔g6
3.♘xf6+–]

2.♗h4+ ♔e6 3.♗xe7+–

■ Puzzle 28

1.♘f7+ ♖xf7 [1...♔e7 2.♘xh8+–]

2.♖a8+ ♔e7 3.♖xh8+−

■ Puzzle 29

1.♗d4+ ♔xd4 2.♕a1+ ♔c5 3.♕xf6+−

■ Puzzle 30

1.♖f6 ♖xa7 2.♖f8+ ♔xd7 3.♖f7+ ♔e6 4.♖xa7+−

■ Puzzle 31

1.♗e5+ ♔xe5 2.♕f4+ ♔e6 3.♕xc7+−

■ Puzzle 32

1.e5+ ♕xe5 [1...♔xe5 2.♘c4+ ♔d5 3.♘xd6+−]

2.♘g4+ ♔e6 3.♘xe5+−

■ Puzzle 33

1.e5+ ♔xe5 [1...♕xe5 2.♘d7+ ♔f5 3.♘xe5+−] 2.♗f4+ ♔e4 3.♗xd6+−

■ Puzzle 34

1.♘d5+ ♗xd5 2.♖a7+ ♔d6 3.♖xe7 ♔xe7 4.♗xd5+−

■ Puzzle 35

1.♗xc5+ ♕xc5 [1...♔xc5 2.♕f8+ ♔b6 3.♕xb4++−]

2.♕f8+ ♔e6 3.♕xc5+−

■ Puzzle 36

1.♖a7+ ♕xa7 2.♕a1+ ♔b5 3.♕xa7+−

■ Puzzle 37

1.h5+ ♔xh5 [1...♕xh5 2.♕g7#]

2.♕h7+ ♔g4 3.♕xh2+−

■ Puzzle 38

1.♘d5+ ♖xd5 2.♖h7+ ♔d6 3.♖a6+ ♕c6 4.♖h6++−

■ Puzzle 39

1.♖f7+ ♕xf7 2.♕a7+ ♔c6 3.♕xf7+−

■ Puzzle 40

1.♘d6+ ♖xd6 [1...♔f8 2.♘xb7+−]

2.♕h7+ ♔f6 3.♕xb7+−

Chapter 10

■ Puzzle 1

1.f6 ♗xf6 2.♕xf6+−

■ Puzzle 2

1.g6 ♗xg6 2.♗xg6+−

■ Puzzle 3

1.♕e4 f5 [1...♗f6 2.♕xh7#]

2.♕xh4+−

■ Puzzle 4

1.♕e2 ♘d6 [1...♗f6 2.♕xb5+−]

2.♕xe7+−

■ Puzzle 5

1.♔g3 ♖d2 2.♔xh3+−

■ Puzzle 6

1.♗b5 ♕xb5 2.♘c7+ ♔f8 3.♘xb5+−

■ Puzzle 7

1.♖xd6+ ♖xd6 2.e5+ ♔e7 3.exd6++−

■ Puzzle 8

1.♗xg7+ ♔xg7 2.♘f5+ ♔g8 3.♘xd6+−

■ Puzzle 9

1.♖xf7+ ♔xf7 2.♘e5+ ♔f8 3.♘xg4+−

■ Puzzle 10

1.♕a6+ ♗f6 [1...♔f7 2.♕a2++−; 1...♔h7 2.♕d3++−]

2.♕d3+ ♔g7 3.♕xb1+−

■ Puzzle 11

1.♗xf7+ ♔xf7 2.♘e5+ ♔g8 3.♘xc6+−

■ Puzzle 12

1.♕xh7+ ♔xh7 2.exf8♘+ ♔g8 3.♘xe6+−

■ Puzzle 13

1.b4 ♞b7 2.b5+−

■ Puzzle 14

1.♜e5 ♞d6 [1...♝g6 2.♜xb5+−]

2.♜xh5+−

■ Puzzle 15

1.♜e7 ♞xd3 2.♜xe8++−

■ Puzzle 16

1.♛d1 ♞f6 [1...♝b4 2.♛xh5+−]

2.♛xd6+−

■ Puzzle 17

1.♝d6 ♜e8 2.♝xb4+−

■ Puzzle 18

1.♚b5 ♜a5+ 2.♚xc6+−

■ Puzzle 19

1.♛e7 ♜c8 2.♛xh4+−

■ Puzzle 20

1.♛a5 ♜c8 2.♛xd2+−

■ Puzzle 21

1.♜xd5 ♜xd5 2.♛e6+ ♚h7 3.♛xd5+−

■ Puzzle 22

1.♜e5 ♚g6 2.♜xa5+−

■ Puzzle 23

1.♝f5 ♜b8 2.♝xg4+−

■ Puzzle 24

1.♜e5 ♛f4 2.♜xb5+−

■ Puzzle 25

1.♜xe7+ ♜xe7 [1...♚xe7 2.d6+ ♚d7 3.dxc7++−]

2.d6 ♜d7 3.dxc7+−

■ Puzzle 26

1.♚e5 ♞g8 2.♜d6+ ♚c5 3.♜xe6+−

■ Puzzle 27

1.♗f3 ♗f6 [1...♘f6 2.♖xe7+−]

2.♗xh5+−

■ Puzzle 28

1.♘e3 ♗h5 [1...♗e7 2.♘xg4+−]

2.♖xd6+−

■ Puzzle 29

1.♗f3 ♘e5 [1...♖d2 2.♗xg4+−]

2.♗xd1+−

■ Puzzle 30

1.♘d4 ♗e4+ [1...♖b1 2.♖e8+ ♔h7 3.♘xf5+−]

2.♖xe4 dxe4 3.♘xb3+−

■ Puzzle 31

1.♘g1 ♕e4 2.♘xe2+−

■ Puzzle 32

1.♖c2 ♗d5 2.♖xe2+−

■ Puzzle 33

1.♕d3 g6 [1...♗c6 2.♕xh7#]

2.♕xd7+−

■ Puzzle 34

1.♗d6 f6 2.♗xc7+−

■ Puzzle 35

1.♕a5 ♗d5 2.♕xc7 ♗xf3 3.♗xf3 ♕xf3 4.♕xd8++−

■ Puzzle 36

1.♖xe5 ♖xe5 2.♘f3 f4 [2...♖xg3 3.♘xe5+−]

3.gxf4+−

■ Puzzle 37

1.g4 ♗g6 2.f4 ♘d7 3.f5+−

■ Puzzle 38

1.♖xa7 ♖xa7 2.♕d4 ♖e2 3.♕xa7+−

■ Puzzle 39

1.b4 ♗xb4 2.♕g4+ ♕g6 3.♕xb4+−

■ Puzzle 40

1.b4 cxb3 2.♖xa6+−

Test #1

■ Puzzle 1

1.♕g4#

■ Puzzle 2

1.♕xe6+ fxe6 [1...♕e7 2.♕xe7#]

2.♗g6#

■ Puzzle 3

1.♘b5#

■ Puzzle 4

1.♕xb8+ ♕xb8 2.♘b6#

■ Puzzle 5

1.♖a4#

■ Puzzle 6

1.♖c7+ ♔xc7 2.d6+ ♕xd6 [2...♔xd6 3.♗b4+ ♔e6 4.♗xe7=] 3.♗f4 ♕xf4=

■ Puzzle 7

1.♕h8+ ♔xh8 2.♘xf7+ ♔g7 3.♘xd6+−

■ Puzzle 8

1.♕g2+ ♗xg2 2.♗xe6+ ♔g7 3.♘xg2+−

■ Puzzle 9

1.g6+ ♔xg6 [1...♕xg6+ 2.♗e4+−] 2.♗h5+ ♔f6 3.♗xf7+−

■ Puzzle 10

1.♗d2 ♘c6 2.♕e6+ ♔h8 3.♕xd5+−

Test #2

■ Puzzle 1

1.♗f3#

■ Puzzle 2

1.♕xh7+ ♔xh7 2.♖h5#

■ Puzzle 3

1.♘f4#

■ Puzzle 4

1.♕b8+ ♖xb8 2.♘c7#

■ Puzzle 5

1.♘f6#

■ Puzzle 6

1.d4+ ♔xd4 [1...♕xd4 2.♗f2 ♕xf2=]

2.♗c3+ ♔d3 [2...♔xc3=]

3.♗xe5 ♗xe5=

■ Puzzle 7

1.♖h8+ ♔xh8 2.♘f7+ ♔g8 3.♘xd6+−

■ Puzzle 8

1.♗h7+ ♔xh7 2.♕xd5+−

■ Puzzle 9

1.♖f8+ ♕xf8 2.♖xf4+ ♔g7 3.♖xf8+−

■ Puzzle 10

1.♕h5 ♖d2+ 2.♔e1 ♖d8 3.♕xf7+−

Test #3

■ Puzzle 1

1.♛b3#

■ Puzzle 2

1.♞h6+ ♛xh6 [1...gxh6 2.♛f8#; 1...
♚h8 2.♛f8#]

2.♛f8#

■ Puzzle 3

1.♞c7#

■ Puzzle 4

1.♛b8+ ♜cxb8 2.♞c7#

■ Puzzle 5

1.♜g6+ ♚xg6 2.♝f5#

■ Puzzle 6

1.♜d2+ exd2+ [1...♚a1 2.♜xd3 e2+
3.♚c2 e1♛ 4.♜a3#]

2.♚d1 ♚b3= [2...♝e5 3.♚xd2=]

■ Puzzle 7

1.♜h8+ ♚xh8 2.♞xg6+ ♚g7
3.♞xh4+−

■ Puzzle 8

1.♝b3 ♚f8 2.♝xf7+−

■ Puzzle 9

1.♜e8+ ♚g7 [1...♜xe8 2.♛xd4+−]

2.♛xd4+ ♜xd4 3.♜xa8+−

■ Puzzle 10

23.♛a5 ♞e6 24.♛xf5+−

Test #4

■ **Puzzle 1**

1.♞b5#

■ **Puzzle 2**

1.♛xg7+ ♚xg7 2.♜g6#

■ **Puzzle 3**

1.♞ce4#

■ **Puzzle 4**

1.♛b8+ ♜xb8 2.♞c7#

■ **Puzzle 5**

1.♝g6+ ♚xg6 [1...♚g8 2.♝h7#]

2.♜g7#

■ **Puzzle 6**

1.♜f8 d6 [1...♛xf8=]

2.♜e8 ♛xe8=

■ **Puzzle 7**

1.♜h8+ ♚xh8 2.♞xf7+ ♚g8
3.♞xd6+−

■ **Puzzle 8**

1.♛b5+ ♜xb5 2.♝xd6+ ♚b7 3.axb5+−

■ **Puzzle 9**

1.♞e6+ ♜xe6 2.♝b2+ ♚e3 3.♝xg7+−

■ **Puzzle 10**

1.♛h1 ♚g6 [1...♞f3 2.♛xh5++−]

2.♛xe1+−

Test #5

■ Puzzle 1

1.♕e5#

■ Puzzle 2

1.♔d2+ ♖g7 2.♖e8#

■ Puzzle 3

1.♕g6#

■ Puzzle 4

1.♕b7+ ♗xb7 2.cxb7#

■ Puzzle 5

1.♘xe4+ ♔e6 2.♘c5#

■ Puzzle 6

1.♖f3+ ♕xf3 2.♘d2+ ♗xd2=

■ Puzzle 7

1.♖h7+ ♔xh7 2.♕xf6+−

■ Puzzle 8

1.♗xf7+ ♔xf7 2.e6+ ♗xe6 3.♕xa5+−

■ Puzzle 9

1.♗xe5+ ♔xe5 [1...♕xe5 2.♕h8+ ♔g6 3.♕xe5+−]

2.♕a5+ ♔f6 3.♕xh5+−

■ Puzzle 10

1.♖c8+ ♔h7 [1...♗f8 2.♗c5+−]

2.♖h8+ ♔g6 3.♖h1 ♘c2 [3...♗e2 4.♖xe1+−]

4.♖xd1+−

Test #6

■ Puzzle 1

1.♖b7#

■ Puzzle 2

1.♘f5+ gxf5 2.♗f8#

■ Puzzle 3

1.♘a5#

■ Puzzle 4

1.♕g8+ ♖xg8 2.♘xf7#

■ Puzzle 5

1.♗e7+ ♔h5 2.♗f7#

■ Puzzle 6

1.♖xc5 ♕xc5 2.♔h1 ♕xf2=

■ Puzzle 7

1.♕h8+ ♔xh8 2.♘xf7+ ♔g7 3.♘xg5+−

■ Puzzle 8

1.♕xd5 exd5 2.exd6+ ♗e6 3.dxc7+−

■ Puzzle 9

1.♗f8+ ♕xf8 [1...♔xf8 2.♖h8+ ♔e7 3.♖xb8+−]

2.♕xb4+ ♔e8 3.♖h8 ♕xh8 4.♕b8+ ♔e7 5.♕xh8+−

■ Puzzle 10

1.♕h8+ ♔xh8 2.♘xf7+ ♔g8 3.♘xd6+−

Test #7

■ Puzzle 1

1.d8♘#

■ Puzzle 2

1.♕a8+ ♖b8 2.♗b7#

■ Puzzle 3

1.♕a5#

■ Puzzle 4

1.♕g8+ ♘xg8 2.♘f7#

■ Puzzle 5

1.♖f8+ ♔xf8 2.♘d7#

■ Puzzle 6

1.♗d3 ♕xd3 2.♕xg7+ ♔xg7=

■ Puzzle 7

1.♗h7+ ♔xh7 2.♕xf7+−

■ Puzzle 8

1.♕a5 ♖xb1 2.♕xe5++−

■ Puzzle 9

1.♖c6+ ♕xc6 [1...♔g5 2.h4++−]

2.♖h6+ ♔g5 3.♖xc6+−

■ Puzzle 10

1.♕a7+ ♔xa7 2.bxc8♘+ ♔b7 3.♘xe7+−

Test #8

■ Puzzle 1

1.♘f3#

■ Puzzle 2

1.♕a8+ ♗g8 2.♖h1#

■ Puzzle 3

1.♘g6#

■ Puzzle 4

24.♕xh7+ ♗xh7 25.♘f7#

■ Puzzle 5

1.♘f6+ ♔f8 [1...♔h8 2.♖xh7#]

2.♘xh7#

■ Puzzle 6

1.♕f6 ♔h7 [1...♕xf6=; 1...♖xf6=]
2.♕xg7+ ♖xg7= [2...♔xg7=]

■ Puzzle 7

1.♕xg7+ ♕xg7 2.♖xe7 ♕xd4
3.cxd4+−

■ Puzzle 8

1.♖xe5 ♖xe5 2.♗c3 ♖ae7 3.♖e3 ♔f6
4.f4+−

■ Puzzle 9

1.♗xd6+ ♕xd6 [1...♔xd6 2.♘b5+
♔c6 3.♘xc7+−]

2.♘f5+ ♔e6 3.♘xd6+−

■ Puzzle 10

1.♕e1 ♕c5 [1...♗f6 2.♕xa5+−; 1...♘c4
2.♕xe7+−]

2.b4+−